The Year; *AD 2365* — The Place; *Sahara Desert*

The Well of Souls

by Shane O'Brien

The Well of Souls

by Shane O'Brien

Editorial Consultant: William T. Kersey

British Library Cataloguing in Publication Data
A catalogue record for this book is available from the
British Library.

ISBN   0 9524768 1 9

Enquiries to the Publishers:
Cumorah Hill / Alan Hawshaw Music Ltd.

Cumorah Hill
PO Box 93
HASTINGS
East Sussex
England   TN34 3ZX

Printed by:
Ebenezer Baylis & Son Ltd. Worcester, England

With special appreciation to Bill, Mary, and Granny. The kind of friends that everyone wishes for.

Also to my friend, David Squibb.

CONTENTS

Prologue

The following story deals with the concept of the pre-mortal existence of man. Woven into the fictional scenario are true precepts which pertain to our very existence here.

Who can conceive the nature of a world where the inhabitants are spirit, at the very heart of the galaxy in the presence of the Creator?

Our natural tendency is to judge the entire universe by the package of scientific laws we have today.

Could it be that in spite of all our scientific advancement, we are yet ignorant, to the extent that we don't even know we are ignorant?

No attempt is made therefore to limit the scientific fantasies in the following narrative, to currently known physical laws.

The reader is challenged instead to consider that above this terrestrial plane we call earth, the laws of physics and their associated possibilities must extend far beyond what we know at present.

Before Earth

The sky is brilliant. Alive with colours which evolve amidst a principal element of white light, filling the heavens above Anju-Sorahn.

Instead of clouds there are interactions of spirit, light and glory which generate by-products of resplendence, in appearance like fluid sheets of brass, platinum or highly refined gold which appear, expand, ripple and disappear in endless progressions. The mortal earth to which I will soon go presents nothing like this. Perhaps the nearest comparable thing will be the Aurora Borealis effected by Earth's magnetic interaction with the ionosphere, wherein shafts of mysterious light, in a much more limited spectrum, will streak across the dark polar skies.

Darkness... Darkness. I cannot comprehend it for here there is no night. There is no sun either, to brighten this nightless existence, none is needed. The immensity of space surrounding Anju-Sorahn is full of glory, full of light. Above and below and on every side there is infinite light.

Oh Anju, for so long thou hast been the cradle of my spirit. Standing upon this my abode: my vision extends through a sea of beauty. In the golden sky, birds flock in fluid waves, wherein numberless individuals moving in unison make up a seemingly single soul. They will continue the same activity when they, like myself, go to the mortal earth.

Trees stand in greatness all around and where there are no trees, there are vast plains of prolific foliage. Ferns, vines, grasses and flowers of every imaginable kind adorn and beautify the timeless world of Anju-Sorahn, whose name means "the first estate".

The colours! Oh the colours! Every plant, every tree, every living thing has an aura of its own. By reason of which, an infinite number of spiritual rainbows are seen to radiate, glide, converge, merge and diverge according to the movements of the creatures from which each aura emanates.

Spirits, myriads of them, the individual intelligences of creatures and organisms, inhabit the multiple spheres of existence which envelop this giant orb. An orb so large that a hundred earths could issue from its bosom. These animals, these creatures, are those which shall be placed upon an earth which has been created expressly for the purpose of the progression of intelligences. Anju-Sorahn shall thus be as a well. A well of souls to not only one earth, but many.

We are taught that on the telestial worlds, creatures and men alike shall have little or no knowledge of the source from which they are drawn... Anju-Sorahn.

I move effortlessly across immense fields of colour to visit friends. I have thousands of friends. Not just acquaintances, but dear ones whom I have loved for ages. Our spirits have communed and marvelled together at the wonders, the splendours of creation which our limitless visions have beheld. We have consoled each other about the future progress of our souls, for we are told that it will be perilous but cannot fully comprehend this, having never known the perils of mortality.

It makes me sad to know that when I am called to leave this place, I shall not retain even the faintest remembrance of these my beloved friends. The eternity of our association will be subdued behind an impenetrable veil of forgetfulness. And they in like manner will forget me, when they too enter mortality.

Notwithstanding this concern, my spirit eagerly and anxiously awaits my turn. My turn on Earth wherein experiences shall be mine, which until now I have only been instructed upon, yet still are beyond my comprehension.

Much of our present is occupied in schooling. All things are taught. Instructors are appointed to conduct the learning.

The focus of study in which I am most zealous is the study of light and the uses thereof.

The amorismic field is that which carries the everlasting images. Thus by accessing the continuum, and forcing sequential separations upon the desired vectors, the pasts of worlds may be read in fluid images. Accelerating the gisic field on the other hand, brings future images to view.

Also of great influence is the borchen field which transports matter. By this power, entire worlds may be transported from one end of the galaxy to the other at the speed of borchen light.

The eshekt field has power, when set in an oscillation wave between the nine constituents of its core-spectrum, to disassemble molecular and atomic structures and regroup according to annular preeminence. Moreover, this is the field by which we may effect a visual—thought link to any chosen body of matter, and discerning its atomic structure, influence the object. Attuning our intelligence to the spheric intelligence of these atoms, protons, positrons and neutrons, we may thus command movement, or reorganisation of the object at will.

None of these fields shall be resident over the mortal earth whose orb of light has been designed to give heat, and vortigent light only. Such a simple orb is Earth's sun, made principally of hydrogen and helium gases. Thus two hundred and forty six properties of the glorious light emitted by the governing orb over Anju-Sorahn will not be shed forth upon the mortal earth.

Many other powers also may be operated by the channeling, focusing and acceleration of certain energy fields.

These powers however, are accessible only to those who obtain the Holy

Priesthood. The High Priesthood after the order of the Firstborn. It is baffling how so many of us shall forfeit this bestowal in exchange for mere earthly and physical pleasures.

The leaders continually place utmost emphasis on our "Training for Mortality" courses. This preparation is crucial we are told. The visual previews are enough to convince anyone of the potential perils which await us in mortality.

A study partner, Elisz has been assigned to me. "Your revision method is not very good. I'll show you how to improve upon it", was her first statement to me.

I must admit that although I did not like Elisz very much at first (she can be so bossy), I have grown to value her understanding. For example, the course has recently focused upon "the essentials of the family unit". For me it was very difficult to grasp certain concepts of motherhood in mortality. Elisz however, possesses remarkable comprehension of this. "A mother," Elisz explained, "will achieve miracles in the rearing of her child. A special bond will exist between mother and infant wherein she shall make tremendous personal sacrifices for the soul, or souls entrusted to her."

"When we leave this existence to enter mortality, we shall become newborn souls in the arms of a mortal mother. And notwithstanding the glorious stature of maturity we now possess, we shall become completely infantile. The baby shall be totally helpless, being entirely dependent on the mother."

With unique energy, Elisz rang out with descriptions of the indescribable sensations a mother will experience when her suckling child fixes its gaze of adoration upon her.

As Elisz elatedly expounded upon these things, she came upon an aspect which turned her joy to bitter sorrow. "...Sadly, not every infant will be so fortunate. Some will be unwanted by the mothers to whom they are born. Without the sheltering protection of a loving mother, they will be subject to the searing cruelty of unrighteous mortal monsters."

As we discussed the impending reality that some infants in their helpless first years will suffer the vicious abuse of evil, physically advanced mortals, our conversation was tinged with emotions of sadness.

"Surely there will be some means" I said to Elisz, "by which the innocent infants will be able to defend themselves against these injustices." "No" was her emphatic reply. "Notwithstanding the magnitude of the injustices, the unfortunate ones will be totally subject to cruelty and abuse, and there will be nothing at all they can do to fight back!"

Contemplating this was so disturbing that Elisz and I desired intensely to converse with our Father on the matter. We sought Him in fervent prayer. In response to our call, Elisz and I were carried by His will, unto Him. His resplendent glory reigned as we stood before His blazing throne.

The power and glory of the Father caused reverence and awe to fill our hearts. Rapture filled my soul. As He looked upon us with such love and providence, as is his way, we were taken up and embraced by Him.

The questions which weighed upon us were thus: "Oh Father, how can this be?" "How can it be that in the mortal period, young and helpless infants, wholly innocent, shall become the victims of evil?"

Elisz, full of anxiety implored saying: "The horrors that some will face are appalling. We have seen in the previews that even in the less severe situations, cold-hearted adults will psychologically abuse their young ones.

I saw for example: an innocent four-year-old boy, struck down by the hand of his earthly father for merely picking up the man's communication device out of curiosity. The man shouted at him and with harsh words dealt a crushing blow to the child's emotional stature. After this, there was no remorse from the man. He turned not to the child with kind words of apology, but callously snatched away the device which the young person had been desirous to see and feel, and left the child crying on the floor, while the man resumed his idle pleasure of watching a television."

The child, after self-healing his emotions, went to his mother for comfort and reassurance that there was love for him in that world, but his mother was absent. He searched for her throughout the house with no success. He learned over the days and months that she simply was there sometimes, but more often, not there. The child was asleep when his mother finally came back into the home. Later, when he was awake, she was rushing around in preparation to leave again. The boy came to her with a paper book and sticks of colour. Reaching up to her he sought interaction. He wanted her to stop moving around so fast and use the sticks of colour. She only pushed him aside however, and disappeared through the front doorway. He was alone. Longing for attention and love, he thought of going to the man. Through painful past experience however, he had learned that the man was not to be disturbed when he sat staring at the box of electronic images.

The child was alone in the world. His crying, he learned, was best kept silent and suppressed. He lived in fear of his mortal father and in longing for his absent uncaring mother. And this is the mildest of such cases!"

Elisz communicated all of this to the Father in the instant of a thought.

"Surely there is a better way! Oh Father, we implore thee. All power is in thine hand! Why dost thou not simply organise the mortal societal framework in such a way that this shall not be?" With his loving look upon us, He placed his finger tips upon my forehead, and then touched Elisz in the same manner and spoke within our spirits saying: "My children, gaze with me upon the expanse of eternity." Our vision was then opened. With magnificent comprehension we perceived the eternity of our existence. For so long already, we had existed in Anju-Sorahn. Then, in and beyond our earthly mortal period we would continue to exist. After the mortal period, we saw that the earth was taken in the grip of the Creator and melted with fervent heat, and became new and was sanctified. We saw that the earth became as a diamond. To stand upon the surface thereof was to stand upon a sea of glass amidst everlasting glorious burnings.

We saw that all who ever lived on the earth were resurrected and thereafter, from eternity to eternity, continued to live as immortal beings. Free from all physical pain and discomfort. The fruit of the sorrows endured in mortality now contributed to the everlasting joy and happiness which they possessed.

The logic was suddenly so clear. Throughout our existence in Anju-Sorahn we have never known physical pain, misery, or injustice. In like manner, throughout the immeasurable expanse of eternity to come, as resurrected beings we shall be impervious to pain. And there will be no injustice to inflict sadness and sorrow upon us. We shall have greater power over opposition.

The period of our mortality will be but a mere moment. A flash in the overall course of existence. Yet the consequences and fruits of it, everlasting.

The mortal period is the time when we must see, and experience the bitter.

"My children, even now you are unable to comprehend the blessed state you enjoy. You have no knowledge of the contrary, and a shallow understanding of opposition.

Although in mortality you shall witness dreadful things, and many shall experience merciless injustices, I will take you up afterwards, and through the Redeemer whom I have chosen, shall heal all wounds. Even wounds from the most ghastly deeds committed by the evil upon the innocent, shall be bound up and healed. And be turned to your joy."

These and many other things were brought more fully to my understanding and Elisz also was enlightened in the love of our Father. He then set us back in our resident tenmauk (a unit of measurement on Anju-Sorahn equal to about 40,000 square miles on Earth).

The percipience and comprehension which Elisz and I had gained, is in fact liberally given by our Father unto all the spirits in Anju-Sorahn. However, only those who seek the understanding receive it. (Some of my kindred spirits are stubborn and not readily willing to receive instruction.)

Before Earth

After some recreation at the towers of Onyx, Elisz and I attended a further session of "Training for Mortality." As the members of our group sat upon the grass amidst the beautiful flowers and trees, we commenced an open discussion. The teacher herself was also quite interested for indeed, our instructors will descend and enter mortality like everyone else.

We asked her if we could conduct a survey of opinions among our peers and began comparing opinions. Some universal questions were put forward: "Do you dread the trials that await us in mortality?" "Are you afraid, knowing that the victim of abuse might be yourself?"

The general response to these and similar questions was reassuring. The kindred we questioned were for the most part tremendously eager and felt ready to take on the challenges of mortality.

One girl in particular, Janjiri, says that she has begun to tire of the easy existence we have in Anju-Sorahn and cannot wait for opportunities to develop new talents and skills, in the face of opposition.

Other spirits seemed to be under the illusion that the mortal period would be easy. The prevalent misconception among my kindred has to do with the proportion of time.

In our existence thus far, we have never known the concept of time, as shall be implemented on Earth. To us at present, the so-called "years" we shall spend there appear as nothing more than a brief interval in the everlasting continuum of our existence.

In my opinion, some spirits are over-confident, taking too lightly the council that our mortal period, once embarked upon, will seem an eternity in itself. It just seems so brief from our perspective in Anju-Sorahn.

Since the beginning, the universal sociality of Anju-Sorahn, my birthplace, has been cradled in transcendent tranquillity. Perpetual unchanging serenity is all I have known. The animals have no understanding of fear — for not a single predator exists here.

Even still, the lesser intelligences which are the animals, plants, and microorganisms, remain in perfect harmony within the myriads of their various spheres. Paradoxically though, in the sphere of my kindred, a conflict arises.

The lesser intelligences are the workmanship of the Supreme and Holy Being of the universe. They are his creations: the expressions of his imagination and eternal purposes. However, the intelligences of my sphere share a far greater heritage. We are not merely the creations of Him whose name is sacred, we are his offspring—his literal sons and daughters, his children.

His name we hold in the greatest reverence. He is from all eternity to all eternity. The love and benevolence which emanates from Him perpetually and showers fully upon us, fills our spirits with light and is the nourishing force by which we have existence.

If he were to withdraw entirely, our glorious spirits, which emit a brilliant field of white light, would darken and wither.

He is the very Eternal Father of us all. The glorious labour with which he is engaged, is to bring about our eternal progress and happiness. He has told us this many times and none of us can doubt it, by virtue of the tremendous power of his love which continually radiates into our spirits. We feel it! As though he stands personally beside us through every moment of existence. Such is the essence of dwelling in the presence of God.

And now, decisions must be made: for the dawn of our mortality is nigh. A time of trial and testing awaits. We are told that influences shall lurk below which are not in accordance with the nature of the Eternal Father of spirits, having the potential to overcome us. Insomuch that we might fall eternally from his presence. Oh these are times of new and grave concern in Anju-Sorahn.

Our Father in his infinite grace and compassion does not force any one of us to go down to the mortal Earth. We are given the free agency of choice to stay here for eternity if we wish. Nevertheless, I, like innumerable kindred spirits, have existed in Anju for what seems an eternity already.

There are many things I cannot comprehend at present which will be revealed to me by experience if I go.

We are taught at great length concerning the challenges we will face and the suffering we shall endure in the process of having a physical body added unto us, but this is a small price to pay for the great potential of personal progression which will also come.

I went through a phase wherein I was somewhat troubled in spirit concerning the drastic changes which are soon to unfold in Anju-Sorahn. Soon, in great numbers my brothers and sisters, my friends, will begin going down to fulfill the measure of their mortal probation. We all have our appointed time. The bounds of our habitations are set. Thus it has been shown to me that the term of my probation shall be 72 earth years. This is not to say that at 72 years of age I shall mandatorily expire, but that through the course of my years, my life shall be spared—in spite of perilous circumstances at times, until my 72 years are complete. Thereafter, the natural course of things shall be incumbent upon me. After that marking point, I may survive another ten or fifteen years, or I may meet death on the day of my 72nd birthday. This and many other aspects of our forthcoming mortal period are as blank chapters in a book, waiting to be written.

For example it has been shown to us, that in mortality we could ruin the entire mapping of our appointed term, by ending our life prematurely. The concept of suicide has heretofore been beyond our imagination, for in *Anju-Sorahn* one cannot simply eject himself from existence.

The burden of our trials in mortality will at times be so great, so severe, so distressing, that some of my kindred will turn to this thing called suicide, in a bid to escape. Only to open their eyes on the other side of the veil and find that the problems they were so desperate to escape now appear in their true perspective, as mere temporary challenges, which in any case, would eventually have worked themselves out. Yet the act of self-destruction, and its price, will then weigh eternally upon the unfortunate souls who make this irreversible error. The regret they will feel shall be bitter. So bitter. It makes me tremble to have been warned that this "suicide" shall even cross my mind at times prior to my 29th year, due to immaturity and a troubled heart.

I might also end my life prematurely through foolish actions and carelessness, in which case, I may not qualify for divine preservation as in other perilous situations.

There are so many variables pertaining to mortality that no one should judge and assume too much. Take the issue of suicide for example: though it shall be a dreadful error committed by some upon themselves, and against the will of the Father, with bitter consequences, who is to say that one person's suicide was not brought on by circumstances beyond his control? Perhaps a chemical imbalance in the brain, or the need to escape the heinous acts of an enemy will be the cause. Who is to say? But then who also should dare justify a suicide?

"To be wise in mortality, we must observe the laws and stay clear of the forbidden paths, yet never be so foolish as to assume that we know everything. Therefore, although we shall know that suicide is forbidden, we shall also be wrong to endeavour to decide the end of every poor soul who exits mortality thus. The Father shall delegate all judgment to the Firstborn. He, shall judge the world. It shall be in His hands, not ours, to judge the outcome of the many perplexities and variables of mortality."

"The wise in mortality shall bear in mind always, that not all things are known. Fools will essay to judge the entire universe with no more knowledge than what they can feel with their hands, and see with their eyes, on Earth." Such are the views of Zelahnim.

My descent will not be expedient for some time yet, but I have acquaintances who are due to go in the First-Seal, or in the first thousand of Earth's years. For me it will be much different. I and many of my dearest friends have been appointed labours in the end of the Sixth-Seal. In a time when great pollutions will have spread forth upon the Earth. Pollutions which will be the negative fruits of man's industrialisation of her resources.

One of my most beloved friends is Zelahnim, whom I admire tremendously because of his wisdom, benevolence, and power of faith. We first met at a science exercise in the Schochal Nebula. Zelahnim was conducting the compaction of $\therefore \text{\textit{#}}7$ and $\therefore * \not\in$ elements for the formation of a $2y_2\}^{.98}s$ nucleus. Before a massive audience, Zelahnim gave a marvellous exegesis on the gravitational properties of the $2y\}^{.}$ constant. "This nucleus, at the density of $^{.98}s$, as we have created here, will have sufficient gravity to retain all ruling constituents of the Koloban light spectrum. Thus when such a nucleus is used in the composition of residential and inheritance orbs, it will not be possible for the inhabitants of mortal worlds to view, with sight extension devices, the surface, nor the immediate atmosphere of these orbs. Of course wave frequencies also cannot escape the pre-determined radius of the $2\}^{.98}s$ nucleus, thus preserving the controlled level of knowledge limitation which must be maintained on certain mortal worlds. They will not be able to detect the existence of inhabitants on orbs cloaked thus."

In a separate journal from this, I have kept notes from nearly all the participatory workshops I have attended, many of which Zelahnim has conducted.

The bond of our friendship has grown strong over the paces of present which have passed. Recently, my soul abounded with unspeakable joy when the decree was set, that Zelahnim will receive his mortal birth through me! I shall serve as engenderer and earthly father for him. This is of great importance and value to me, for in giving mortal birth to him, our lineal relationship shall be established for eternity, if we follow the directions of the Father.

As I think of my friend Zelahnim, whose mortal infancy shall be entrusted to me, it strikes an overwhelming sensation within my soul to contemplate how this great one, this giant of spirit — for so consider I him to be — will become my son on Earth. Here in Anju- Sorahn I have listened to his views with eagerness to learn and I have emulated his greatness. But on Earth, he shall become a babe in my arms. An infant whom I shall train and teach. An adolescent whom I shall endure and forgive. And most hopefully, an adult whose former spiritual greatness shall have carried him safely through his impressionable and immature years of mortality into stable paths of righteousness.

I have been warned however, that if I proceed in mortality to make the wrong choices, and allow the vain ambitions and pursuits of earthly rewards to possess my heart, I will miss and forfeit my sacred appointment of bringing Zelahnim into the world and of raising him in the right ways.

As I cast my vision beyond the Kyrianton forest, which is where I often go to walk and think in solitude about the course of my existence, I see great multitudes gathered together, listening to one whom they think is wise —but he is a deceiver. He lies to them. Why can they not see this? Why do they follow him? His name is Lucifer and he opposes the Eternal Father by endeavouring to impose an alternate plan for the probation of our spirits on the mortal earth. Lucifer is known throughout Anju-Sorahn. It has been terribly disruptive, this rebellion he has led — for he is, or was, one of the governing ones. His authority was of the High Order and would still have been if not for his defiant and rebellious heart. The Father has issued a directive throughout Anju that Lucifer's position of authority in which we have always known him is no longer valid.

A solemn warning has spread to every tenmauk not to follow Lucifer for he seeks only to glorify himself. Following him, we are told, would be fatally detrimental to our progress. It is known that he is one of the eldest of all the spirits, which is partly the reason for his level of achievement. However, he is not the eldest.

The Anointed One is the first born spirit of our Eternal Father. He and the Father are as one. He whose name is Jehovah is the chosen one who shall serve as the Mediator. Appointed to go in the meridian of time to receive his physical body, at which time he shall fulfill the requirements of the Father and make an infinite intercession for all mankind. He, the First-born, shall be the Saviour of the world.

He shall be the holiest of all. He shall be the Only Begotten of the Father on Earth and be known as the Son of God. Notwithstanding this, they shall crucify him.

No mortal man in all of Earth's history shall have power in and of himself to resurrect his own body from the grave to an immortal state. But the Son of God shall have power in himself to overcome mortal death. And He, in turn, shall raise all the sons and daughters of men. The glory, majesty, power, and dominion of the First-born surpasses by far, all the other spirits in Anju-Sorahn. The knowledge of him fills my soul with rapture.

Unfortunately Lucifer is envious of His place. In a vile attempt to usurp the glory of the First-born, Lucifer now wages war. And I, a mere spirit among myriads watch in utter amazement as so many of our brothers and sisters hearken to his vain lies.

Recently I was drawn into a very bitter experience when Elah, a close friend of mine, informed me of his decision to join the hosts of Lucifer. I was startled and pleaded with him to come to my place of abode and talk it over with Zelahnim, whom I was sure would be able to convince Elah of the error in his thinking. But Elah would not hearken to me.

He withdrew and with great speed did convey himself to the conference centre of Lucifer's followers. I felt deeply distraught for my spirit had grown to love Elah. I conveyed to the place where he went and casting my vision through the multitudes and discerned him. I went to him. "Elah!", he turned to me and smiled. His friendliness, as it had always been, encouraged me that there was hope.

"Please, come away from here." I implored. To which he replied, "You've got to hear Narcus speak. Stay and hear. Discover the exhilaration of uniting with the new movement. A new age has dawned!"

Now Narcus was a leading emissary and advocate of Lucifer and served in rallying his forces. Elah insisted that if I would stay and listen to Narcus who was about to address the host of spirits assembled at this place, I would then understand.

Elah said: "Narcus will show you why it is right that all the spirits of Anju should join together and uphold *Lucifer* as the chosen one."

"It is within our power to remove the First-born from office! For he does not wield the sword of glory the way *Lucifer* knows it should be done!"

"*Lucifer* will use the power and take us all speedily to the highest heights of glory! And we shall not be given the chance to fail!"

My spirit was trembling. I could not believe that I was hearing *Elah* say such things — and I certainly did not want to hear *Narcus* give his tirade, for to begin with, *Lucifer* is a liar. He does not have the power that he claims. He has not the power to give us tangible bodies and through mortality raise us to immortality, to be eternal, incorruptible souls like unto our *Father*.

I leaned close to *Elah* saying: "Come away with me now: I insist!" I wanted to take hold of his arm to bring him out. At this he rejected me. Our conversation was perceived by others of the pressing multitude.

Suddenly, a large and proud spirit proclaimed in a loud voice: "What do we have here! An advocate of the First-born?" The attention of the surrounding congregation was now focused upon me. They began to contend with me vehemently, shouting blasphemies against the Anointed One, the First-born. They began pressing in upon me with the intent to cause distress. I was overwhelmed! But then, a familiar voice came into my soul. Zelahnim my beloved friend spoke to me from afar. Having discerned my distress among the hosts of Lucifer, Zelahnim reached unto me with the voice of his spirit — which became a strength unto me and I broke away from them. I came straight away to Zelahnim. Trembling from the ordeal I began to weep. The taste of bitter experience lodged within me. Through my tears I looked at Zelahnim who, smiling peacefully, held his hand out to me and said: "I thought you

knew better than to go in amongst the
armies of *Lucifer* at their gatherings." I
embraced and thanked him for being a
strength to me. He looked into my eyes and
said: "I suppose you will have the chance
to return the favour. On the mortal
Earth when I, in my tender years am in
your care, perhaps I shall naively fall in
among the advocates of *Lucifer* as you
have done this present. If this should
happen, I pray that you will seek after
me and draw me out as I have sought
after you this day."

I was weeping still, for my spirit was
full of emotion and turning to *Zelahnim*,
I spoke within him by the voice of my
spirit saying: "I promise, I will watch
over you."

The solemnity of this moment was soon
carried away upon wings of good cheer
when a group of our friends soared by in
recreation, inviting us to go diving with
them at the crystal sea.

There is an abyss there which we fly into. Progressing through its depths we behold many creatures of different types.

As I rejoice in the company of friends, there is yet a trembling within my spirit, echoing the war which has torn the fabric of perfect serenity in Anju-Sorahn, and the ordeal of my mortal probation which looms ahead. But I would not have it any other way. I and my brethren will shout for joy when the Earth is ready, and the sons and daughters of God will sing together.

❖   ❖   ❖

The concept of a "pre-mortal" existence, as portrayed in the foregoing fictional scenario carries a number of compelling implications to say the least.

Is it possible that we could have existed as spirits — before being born into this life?

A qualified response to this question may be developed upon consideration of the facts involved in thousands of "near-death experiences" which have been documented. Within these experiences is sound evidence that the human soul consists of two principal aspects: The physical body and the spirit. The body, of course, is mortal at present and will experience death. The spirit on the other hand is eternal and does not expire at the time of physical death. We shall explore the tangible evidence of this in the ensuing chapter.

A point of logic may be raised here: If indeed the spirit continues to live beyond the death of the body, that same spirit could just as well have existed prior to mortal birth.

In approaching a subject such as this we inevitably enter the dreaded field of religion. "Dreaded" by reason of the tremendous furor caused by religion—in men's hearts as well as on a larger scale, in the form of wars between nations. Nevertheless, here we are.

In the Bible there are scriptural references which allude to this pre-mortal existence. For example Jeremiah 1:5 reads:

> Before I formed thee in the belly I knew thee; and before thou camest forth out of the womb I sanctified thee, and I ordained thee a prophet unto the nations.

Notwithstanding this and other Biblical references to the same effect, the only Christian church which has any substantial doctrine on the subject is the Church of Jesus Christ of Latter-Day Saints. The concept of the pre-mortal existence in relation to the present mortal period may be summarised thus:

> *All people are the sons and daughters of God, born as his literal offspring long before this Earth was created. We grew and matured as spirits, but had not yet acquired the tangible, physical aspect we now possess. For an untold, unknown expanse of time, we existed there in the pre-mortal world, learning and progressing until it became expedient for us to enter a period of mortal probation at which time we were born into this life and received a physical body.*

Among the several reasons for our entry into this life are the following main purposes:

- ❖ To gain a physical body.
- ❖ To prove obedience and faithfulness to our eternal Heavenly Father.
- ❖ To gain experience.
- ❖ To develop qualities such as faith and charity.

This life is meant to be a trial and a test. Therefore with our mortal body comes also a veil of forgetfulness. For indeed, if we could clearly recall our pre-mortal existence the conditions of the test we are now in would be drastically altered.

On the basis of this "before earth" concept we encounter some rather compelling implications. For example, consider the children that are born to us: Is it not possible that these were friends, or people we had known for a very long time before coming here?

I wonder what great promises might have been exchanged between many of us, which have now been forgotten. I wonder how many parents have mistreated children who in the pre-mortal existence had actually been their greatest friends.

Considering the details in the *"Before Earth"* story, further comment is requisite.

The endeavour of presenting a dramatised scenario of the pre-mortal existence poses a number of inherent complications. For such an existence would have been so completely different from what we, in mortality, know as day to day life, that much of what might be said in the scenario would in fact be erroneous in context. For example; if the writer of the story wanted to say something like, "yesterday, I went to the Kyrianton forest," it could thus be argued that in the pre-mortal existence there was no such thing as *yesterday*, at least as we know it. Some might say that there was no sun rising and setting to mark the beginning and end of each day, yet this also could be argued. Maybe there was a system of reckoning segments of time in days. Who knows? Another example: In the story, the central figure at one point cries "tears of bitterness." Can a spirit cry bitter tears? I don't know.

While the fundamental framework of the *Before Earth* story is based on the doctrine of the pre-mortal existence, as contained in the teachings of the Church of Jesus Christ of Latter-Day Saints, it must be emphasised here that the story is fictitious and is not doctrine of the Church. Nevertheless, intrinsic in the story is a thought provoking scenario which does indeed pivot upon reality.

As for the discussion about light, it is of course purely fanciful. It is possible however, that other types of light exist beyond our solar system, of which we are unaware. Light with extraordinary properties. Within the limits of our present technology, the concepts of laser power and fibre optics clearly demonstrate the far reaching potential of light as a powerful medium.

Laying aside all speculative details, the concept of the pre-mortal existence is of tremendous value in raising a true, over-arching perspective of what this life is all about. As mentioned earlier, dynamic support for such a thesis may be derived from the fact that in a variety of crisis situations, millions of people have discovered that the spirit within us lives on, beyond the threshold of death, independant of the body.

Out of literaly thousands of near-death experiences which have been documented, one which towers above most others in terms of the depth of what the experiencer was allowed to learn, is the experience of Betty J. Eadie, who tells her story in *Embraced by The Light*.

Significantly, Mrs Eadie speaks clearly in her account of the "pre-mortal" existence, according to what was revealed to her through the course of her excursion in the spirit world:

> All people as spirits in the pre-mortal world took part in the creation of the earth. We were thrilled to be part of it.
>
> ... Each spirit who was to come to earth assisted in planning the conditions on earth, including the laws of mortality which would govern us. These included the laws of physics as we know them, the limitations of our bodies, and spiritual powers that we would be able to access. We assisted God in the development of plants and animal life that would be here. Everything was created of spirit matter before it was created physically...
>
> ...I saw that in the pre-mortal world we knew about and even chose our missions in life... Through divine knowledge we knew what many of our tests and experiences would be, and we prepared accordingly.

Embraced by The Light 1992 p.47

The Spirit and the Body

The belief that our spirits had an existence prior to mortal birth is profoundly sustained by the concept of the near-death experience, or NDE. The basic situation in these cases is:

> A person is involved in a severe accident, or medical emergency, during the course of which they essentially die. Or to be more exact; the extreme injury and stress incurred by the victim is sufficient to cause the separation of the spirit from the body. In these cases however, it is not yet expedient for the mortal period of such individuals to end, hence they are ushered back into their bodies.

A survey in 1982 showed that in the United States alone, approximately eight million adults reported having near-death, out-of-body experiences. Moreover, a remarkable degree of common phenomena prevails between such accounts, as summarised in the following:

❖ The person suddenly finds himself floating in the air, able to look down and see his body.

❖ An immediate, complete cessation of all pain, discomfort and anxiety occurs. Instead there is a transcendent feeling of peace and well-being.

❖ For some, the experience terminates here as they are instantly drawn back into the body. Thus they have had only a momentary separation of body and spirit.

❖ Those who are given a slightly longer excursion on the other side of mortality report finding themselves in a dark tunnel, progressing steadily toward a beautiful bright light.

 *39*

❖ Entering into the light, the person experiences a tremendous feeling of being embraced in the love of God.

❖ Relatives and friends who had previously passed on come to greet and escort the person.

A phenomenal number of these incidents are being reported, hence we also hear the abundant opinions of skeptics who do not accept the concept of *life after death*.

In the controversy, we encounter various experts who are intent on explaining away NDEs as mere illusions brought on by physiological causes. Lack of oxygen to the brain, sudden release of endorphins and excessive levels of carbon dioxide in the blood are typical of the "perfectly logical" explanations held aloft by the illustrious skeptics.

I agree that lack of oxygen, and other trauma related effects are capable of causing altered states of consciousness. I agree that cases do occur wherein people claim to have had spiritual experiences, which have actually been fantasized or fabricated for various reasons. I do not agree however, with the closed book approach of many "experts", who would rather believe just about any explanation for NDEs other than what those who have actually had the experience are telling us.

The genuine cases of near-death/out-of-body experiences are not the product of a withering brain. They are not merely an imaginary state of mind. They are a momentary departure of man's eternal spirit from his fragile mortal body. The weight of evidence defies all the scientists and all the scholars in the world who assay to prove otherwise.

I personally have never had an NDE and hope I never do, as they tend to come about as a result of perilous or life threatening circumstances. Nevertheless, I have come into direct contact with various people who have been there. Some of these individuals have agreed to let me recount their experiences in this book:

Elana

Sunday afternoon, the 11th of March 1992, held unexpected turns for Elana and her boyfriend Simon.

After a quiet social visit with another friend at Elana's home in Bexhill, East Sussex, they went in Simon's new car to take their friend back to his home, at which time the following events occurred as related to me by Elana: "We were driving towards Battle (near Hastings), taking a friend home. Simon was going too fast. I suppose he was showing off a bit. Anyway, we got to the bend at St Mary's Cottages and the next minute, the car hit the curb and somersaulted." Elana apparently was knocked unconscious at this point, because she recalls coming to and finding herself trapped in the wreckage. She recalls seeing Simon pinned behind the wheel and paramedics (presumably) working to free him. At this point she also realised that men were cutting away at her side of the car.

After this moment of awareness, Elana lost consciousness again. "I don't remember the journey back to the hospital but just remember being in casualty, and, trying to see my arm and what was wrong with it. It was all hustle bustle and all this noise and everyone (the hospital staff) was rushing about. I remember just lying there, trying to fathom out what was going on. I can remember just shutting my eyes and thinking, oh no this... I don't know... I can't... it was such an awful feeling and pain and noise. Then all of a sudden I was just up in the corner of the emergency room and I could see everything, it was, it was really a lovely, lovely feeling and I could see me, in one bed and they were stitching my head up. And Sharon (the nurse) was pushing on my chest to start me breathing again. Simon was in another bed and Andrew in the other one, and everyone hustling and bustling about. It was weird though because I knew I was out of my body. I had heard of this on television and you know when you hear it you just think, oh another nutter, but when it happens to you you know precisely what they're on about, and it is special to you, and private in a way."

Elana also explained that while out of the body, there was a golden or warm light emanating from somewhere, at which point she emphasised again that she felt "perfect, calm and with no worries you just knew what was going on and everything made perfect sense. And then the next minute I can remember opening my eyes and hitting reality, at least the reality of being here again, and thinking Oh my God I've been shoved back."

Anna

On December 26th, 1993 Anna was enjoying a social afternoon with friends when she collapsed. Her condition was obviously severe to those around her, hence an ambulance was called immediately.

Anna was rushed to Conquest Hospital in Hastings, East Sussex, then to Hurstwood Park neurological centre. She had a couple of X-rays and it was determined that her affliction was a brain haemorrhage. Up to this time, throughout the ordeal she had been going through extreme pain. Anna was given a general anaesthetic and her skull was opened for brain surgery.

During this operation, she suddenly found herself awake, up in the air, towards the ceiling of the operating theatre.

Looking down upon everything that was going on, she recalls seeing four or five doctors carrying out the operation. She saw her exposed brain. However, none of this caused any stress whatsoever, as she felt totally calm and peaceful. "I felt safe" Anna told me. Moreover, the searing pain which she had been enduring was now entirely non-existent. At this moment of tranquillity, Anna was suddenly drawn back into her body at which point she was again under the anaesthetic.

After the operation, when she had regained consciousness, Anna could remember the extraordinary experience. She wanted to speak of it, but who would believe her?

John

In Middlesbrough, England, I interviewed a man who like Anna rose out of his body while under anaesthetic. In 1979, John was living in Redcar, Cleveland. He needed extensive dental surgery which warranted total anaesthesia.

Reclining in the dentist chair at Thurland and Corner dental practice, he was instructed by the anaesthetist to count to 10. John does not recall reaching the tenth count, but his body started to struggle violently through an averse reaction to the anaesthetic. Next thing he knew, he was floating in the air in the upper part of the room, and found that while no longer possessing a tangible physical body, he still did have a spiritual body. "I saw that I had hands, feet, legs, and arms..."

In his disembodied state, John was fully aware and conscious of everything that was going on around him. He experienced a tremendous feeling of peace and warmth — unlike anything he had ever known in life, and did not want to come back. This particular detail came up several times during our interview.

He was carried into a waiting room where proper attention could be given. Soon, the doctors as well as his mother who was present began to show grave concern, as they could not revive him. John told me, *"I know why they couldn't revive me, It's because I didn't want to come back."*

The sense of well-being he experienced was so great that it seemed pointless and unfavourable to come back and continue with his life. Nevertheless, John was made aware that it was important for him to return to mortality. There were purposes for him to yet fulfill. Accepting this, he was drawn back into his body.

"I learned from it, that our spirit body is like our own body. And that there is life after death... But I didn't want to come back."

Sharon

Another typical case is that of Sharon, a mother of three who in January of 1980 was almost killed in a tragic automobile accident. However, it was not her time to go, and after a short excursion on the other side, she too was ushered back into her body.

The experience was so extraordinary and left such a great impact upon Sharon that as soon as sufficient recovery from her injuries was made, she wrote a detailed account of what transpired.

At the time of the crash her spirit rose immediately out and above the wreckage. There was no pain, panic, or fear.

When the paramedics and other persons arrived, she observed peacefully as they frantically rushed about dealing with the emergency.

Sharon began to pass through what must be a sort of veil between this mortal arena and the spirit world, which apparently encompasses the Earth. She was very happy and eager to move on into this spiritual realm, however a voice spoke to her saying: "You know you must go back." "*Can't I stay?*" she replied. Then suddenly, a statement filled her being: "What about your two young sons?" For an instant Sharon pondered this fact, and swiftly resolved; "*They'll be all right, Terry, will take care of them.*" Terry was her husband whom she was also leaving behind in mortality. In spite of leaving these loved ones, she was desirous to complete the transition and remain in the spirit world. Again she was urged to go back, which she did.

Karen

A number of cases have come to my attention in which women have momentarily risen out of their bodies during the throes of travail or other complications relating to pregnancy and childbirth. An example of this may be drawn from the experience of Karen, mother of four, who ran into complications during pregnancy with her 3rd child. She was in St. Thomas hospital of Westminster and suddenly haemorrhaged. The first thing she recalls was that she heard her mother, in a panic, calling her name. Then, Karen suddenly realised that she was up above everyone. She tried to tell her mother that she was okay, but no one in the room could hear, or see her. They were trying to get a response from a person lying there, which already seemed to Karen as nothing more than a likeness of her. Even though it had been her body, Karen felt like saying; "That's not me there Mum! I'm here, up here!" She was suddenly thereafter drawn back into her body.

When Karen spoke with me, she explained that prior to this experience she really did not have any particular belief in God. She had always thought that people who claimed to have an experience like this were imagining it somehow. But now, a profound new outlook has come to her. Is there life after death? Karen will tell you there is.

❖   ❖   ❖

Further to the several cases of near-death experiences associated with pregnancy and childbirth which I personally know of, there are many examples published in various books and reports on the subject. One such book is *Return from Death* by Margot Grey, from which I give the following excerpts: [1]

A woman whose near-death event had resulted from a prolonged and difficult labour during childbirth gave the following account: "As the pain reached its peak it suddenly stopped and I found myself suspended up under the ceiling... Although I couldn't see my body (because of something which was blocking her view), I could nevertheless see everything in the room, like the telephone which was not visible from the bed, I could see quite clearly from my position above. I could also hear everything that was going on and the nurse who was still trying to get me to move my leg. Then I heard her say, 'My God, she's gone.'"

Another case in *Return from Death* deals with a woman who haemorrhaged following an operation for the removal of fibroid tumors in her womb: [2]

I remember coming round from the anaesthetic and then drifting off and finding myself out of my body, over the bed looking down at my carcass... I could see the doctors and nurses round my bed frantically trying to give me a blood transfusion. They were having difficulty finding a vein in my arm. I was amused at all this fuss going on with my body as it did not concern me a bit.

Another book; *Beyond Death's Door* by Dr. Maurice Rawlings, published in 1978 contains the following report which concerns a lady in her twenties who came out of her body after giving birth: [3]

I had lost a lot of blood. It was about an hour after I had delivered my only child. When they moved me from the stretcher to the bed to take me to surgery I could see the blood pouring through the gap between the bed and stretcher. It seemed to spurt each time my heart beat. It was an incredible loss of blood. I was sure my time was up.

They rushed me down to the operating room with blood splattering on the floor. When I arrived in the operating room I suddenly wasn't in my body. I don't remember getting out of it. But at least it didn't hurt. I was floating in the left-hand corner of the ceiling looking down at my doctor. I didn't like him. He was cursing and yelling at the nurses. I think he was panicked over my condition. Now I was sure I was going to die.

They were getting ready to give me an injection of medicine to put me to sleep but I was sure I would die before they could stop my bleeding. I saw the faces of my mother, husband, and baby boy who were all living. They would be sad at my death but I didn't feel despondent. In fact, it didn't seem to make much difference to me at all. I wasn't unhappy and I couldn't understand why.

Next, I was hurtling down this dark tunnel at a high speed, not touching the sides. It made sort of a swishing sound. At the end of the tunnel was this yellow-white light. And then I said, 'This must be what it feels like to die. I feel no pain at all.' I was glad of that. But before I could get to the light and out of the tunnel, I found myself back in the recovery room that had four beds in it and I was in one of them.

I will never forget the peacefulness that I experienced. For some reason I was not afraid of this dying business, but I was glad to see my baby boy again!'

❖   ❖   ❖

One fine summer evening, I stood conversing with my neighbour about random subjects. He told me of his mother who in 1964 was staying at St Bartholomew's Hospital in London due to several illnesses. Complications arose which brought her very near to the point of death. During this situation her spirit rose out of her body and she found herself floating at the top of the room—looking down and seeing herself laying in the bed. For years after, she maintained her story of this experience, but people simply attributed this "delusion" to her ill condition.

We may also consider the case of Austin Tatham, a West Indian man from Trinidad who at 51 years of age had a stroke. He was taken into Northuring Hospital in Bedford. After a few days of laying very ill in bed, he died; sort of.

He suddenly found himself in the upper part of the room and saw his body lying on the bed. In this out-of-body state he felt tremendously calm and tranquil, warm and safe. He wanted to stay in that realm, but was told that his time was not yet. Austin came back, knowing that he had some time left to put various things in order. He died a year later of a heart attack.

Throughout the final year of Austin's life, he was notably happy and well oriented for leading a full and productive life.

Jackie

I recently had the opportunity of interviewing a lady who had a near-death experience which came about as a result of an illness in which her gall bladder ceased to function.

A crisis developed which culminated in her being rushed into East Sussex Hospital. Jackie recalls feeling the cold winter air on her face as she was carried out of her home to the ambulance. She then lost consciousness.

By the time Jackie was taken into the hospital, her vital signs were dangerously low. The medical staff were endeavouring to revive her when she suddenly awoke from her uncon scious state. She awoke and found herself standing near the bed watching the nurse try to get a response from her lifeless body by jabbing her toes with a pointed instrument. Jack ie saw herself lying on the bed, however, she felt a nearly spontaneous disassociation fro m the body which she had left.

During the interview, I was about to ask if she had seen a light or tunnel during the experience, but before I came to it, Jackie said to me: "There was this brilliant, beautiful light off to the side. It's hard to explain because even though I know it was there, and somehow could see it, I didn't dare fully face it or go into it."

The remarkable context of her statements regarding this experience became increasingly apparent when towards the end of the interview I found that she actually had no knowledge of the general occurrences of near-death experiences, in spite of the publicity this subject has received over the past decade.

Jackie thought that she had been privileged to experience and discover something which no one else had.

❖   ❖   ❖

In 1992, an article was published containing an interview with Ms Colleen Haley, who was in a tragic automobile accident in which two of her daughters were killed. Colleen was driving home with her three girls when the following occurred:

> As we got near our driveway, I slowed down, unfastened my own seat belt and flipped on my left-turn indicator. A quick glance in the rear-view mirror assured me that nothing was behind us.
>
> I started to turn when, all of a sudden, a huge blue-and-white truck was right behind us, roaring towards the back of the car. I don't remember the crash; being thrown from the car; or wandering in a daze across my neighbour's lawn.

Colleen remembers seeing Jessica and Jeanette, her two youngest daughters, crushed between the front and back seats, covered in blood, and she could hear Cindy, the eldest, calling out for her. "*I knew Jessica was dead,*" she recalls.

Colleen herself had sustained severe injuries and was in tremendous pain. It appears that at this stage, Colleen's spirit left her body:

> Suddenly, my pain evaporated. I was holding Jessica's hand and walking with her toward a warm, bright and blindingly beautiful light. I knew at that instant; and believe still with all my heart that I was taking my little girl to Heaven.
>
> The next thing I knew, I was lying in a stretcher in the hospital. Jeanette lay on a stretcher nearby.
>
> ...I'll never stop crying over that night...

Tragically, Jeanette had received severe brain damage and died a few hours later.

As Colleen struggles to stop blaming herself for the tragic death of her daughters, it is certain that this extraordinary spiritual experience, seeing her daughter walk peacefully and happily into *"a beautiful light,"* has brought strength and inspiration in coping with the tragedy.

❖   ❖   ❖

Over the past fifteen years there have been several documentaries on television in which near-death experiences have been reported on and discussed. In 1987 I recieved a ticket from an associate who worked at the BBC, to attend one of these broadcasts as a member of the studio audience. Of course there were several people there who gave detailed accounts of their out-of-body experiences. Some inspiring cases were brought to light on that occasion.

A few months later, a much more comprehensive study on the subject was aired on BBC 2, featuring a fascinating investigation conducted by medical experts, who found it peculiar and extraordinary that so many people from different walks of life, were coming out with the same basic story. The strength of this particular study rests in the impeccable parity between the statements of those whose experiences occurred during medical emergencies, and the actual records of the clinicians.

The subjects were able to describe procedures of the doctors which took place when they were in a state of total anaesthesia, and even clinically dead in some cases.

One woman who has been blind for many years, had an out-of-body experience during a complicated operation, and discovered that upon leaving her body, she could see again! During the height of the medical emergency when doctors were fighting to save her, she saw one of them loose his "orange pen" which after hitting the floor slid under a metal cabinet. Subsequently, after being drawn back into her body, having awakened from the operation, she unfortunately found herself still blind. However, the doctors were mystified when this lady told them of the "orange pen which went under the blue metal cabinet." She went on to describe many other details of the scene which she could not have known being blind, in addition to the fact that she was totally unconscious at the time.

In the interview, this blind woman described her highly contrasted emotions when suddenly, she found herself able to see, yet just as suddenly, the gift was taken again from her. The one consolation, she says, is that "I now know that there is life after death, and it is only my physical body which is blind. Even if I never see again in this life, my sight will come back afterward."

DAVID

David Verdegaal is sure he has come back from the dead. In April of 1986, while on a business trip to Austria, he suffered a massive heart attack after checking into a hotel in a village near Innsbruck. An ambulance was called immediately and David was rushed to the University Hospital at Innsbruck where efforts to resuscitate him continued, even though he was clinically dead on arrival.

David Verdegaal's case was featured on another television documentary, this one on ITV in February of 1995. The producers of the programme actually sent a film crew to Austria to show the town, the hotel, and the hospital where all of this took place.

In the hospital, they interviewed Doctors Lotz and Deanstull who explained that David was clinically dead for about 30 minutes. However, in the fourth attempt to resuscitate him with the cardioversion paddles, a faint heart rate appeared on the monitor.

David was then in a coma for two weeks. After coming out of this he proceeded to write out the details of his experience during the time in which he was clinically dead. David recalls:

When I died, the first experience was, seeing a marvelous light. A light but not a light, a light that was a spiritual light, that was transforming.

When it had enveloped you, you were enveloped in love, I was changed - and I felt, renewed, completely.

... It was a moment you know that you could live forever. And from that pure moment, I knew that it didn't really matter if I came back or was to carry on, everything was right, as it should be.

•   •   •

Numerous similar situations were presented in the above cited documentary, in which a series of people were interviewed. Some of their statements are as follows:

1- "I saw the heart monitor stop... it went dead, dead flat. And at that time the nurses called a code blue on me. Everyone was rushing into the room, and I started rising up! Out of my body!..."

2- "I became aware of this table that was brightly illuminated. And apparently, I was 50 feet higher than the table, looking down at this corpse like figure - then I thought - my God! that's me, lying on the table..."

3- "...I found myself up at the corner of the room, up against the ceiling looking down on myself. And I was quite surprised to see how ill I looked... I remember thinking quite clearly to myself - 'so this is what happens when one dies. This is death; this is dying. One is alive, one is conscious, one knows who one is, and yet there was absolutely no fear.'"

4- "I became aware that I was in darkness, and I couldn't really figure out exactly where I was. And shortly after that, it became very bright - beautifully bright."

5- "It was a light that went out not only very far, but folded back on itself. And I was in the heart of this. ...when I was told by this light that I had to go back it was a real shock. I begged to remain in the presence of this light. The magnetic quality of this light is indescribable. To be separated was the most bitter experience I ever had."

6- "I left this world, and came back again. I'm totally convinced of that."

7- "I've had a lot of very powerful emotional experiences in my life. None, come anywhere close, to the near-death experience; to the white light. None of them even touch on that."

8- "Did it change me?! Oh my goodness. It, has shaped my life. It has shaped my entire adulthood."

Dr. Melvin Morse

A prominent author in the field of near-death studies is Dr. Melvin Morse, interviewed in the aforementioned television report. While working as a paediatrician in the critical care unit at the Seattle Children's Hospital, Dr. Morse noticed that in many instances his patients would describe remarkable experiences in which they claimed to have floated out of their bodies — and from up near the ceiling, witnessed the events of their resuscitation. These reports from children motivated Dr. Morse and some of his colleagues to commence systematic research surveys on the subject, which he conducted for over ten years.

One particular case which impressed Dr. Morse involves a five-year-old girl who nearly died of bacterial meningitis. During the crisis in which the doctors almost lost her, Jamie experienced death.

In the televised documentary, Dr. Morse unrolled a painting on a sheet of paper done by the little girl when she was seven, in which she portrayed the scene in the emergency room.

In the painting, Jamie has depicted her body on the table and a physician with his hands properly placed on her chest (at *sternum*) in the resuscitation effort. Up near the ceiling, Jamie depicted herself again, as having risen out of her body. Dr. Morse was impressed with the fact that she also placed a man at the foot of the operating table wearing a conspicuous hat, which is significant because in the operating theatre, says Dr. Morse, the resuscitation team leader always wore a hat in order to be easily recognised in the hubbub and confusion of emergency situations. Also in her painting Jamie depicts the brilliant light she saw during the experience.

In the opening chapter, we discussed the concept that our spirits existed prior to birth into this world. Jamie's comments regarding her experience contain a significant reference pertinent to this doctrine: She was puzzled to have encountered *"people about to be born."* [4]

Reinforcement to this comes to light in a totally unrelated case, involving another little girl, Katie, who was found lying face down in a public swimming pool. Dr. Morse writes, *"No one knew how long she had been unconscious or exactly what had happened to cause her to lose consciousness. ... I was the doctor who resuscitated her in the emergency room after the accident in the pool. Despite all our best efforts, I was sure she was going to die. Still we tried everything we could think of."*

Fortunately, Katie made a full recovery and as recorded in Morse's book *Closer to the Light*, she was able to give a remarkable detailed account of how at the time of her drowning, she passed through a dark tunnel. On the other side, in heaven, she met her late grandfather and other people. Moreover, she told Dr. Morse of *"souls waiting to be born"* whom she had met. [5]

One valuable aspect of Morse's work is that the experiences documented therein are from children. We are dealing with kids who have been on the operating table and have faced medical emergencies. Children too young to have formulated opinions one way or the other about NDEs, or to have studied the subject. They have no religious or scientific axe to grind yet universally, in literally hundreds of unrelated incidents, we discover the consistent testimony of an excursion of the spirit beyond the ailing physical body.

By virtue of the exquisite nature of these experiences, we shall include the following samples. The text from this point to the "end quote" notation on page 56, is quoted from *Closer to the Light* by Dr. Melvin Morse (1992): [6]

June, an eight-year-old girl, nearly drowned in a swimming pool when her hair became caught in the drain. Her parents, an emergency medical team, and finally emergency room doctors gave her CPR for more than forty-five minutes before her heart began beating again. She made a full neurological recovery in less than six weeks.

All I remember was my hair getting stuck in the drain and then blacking out. Then next thing I knew, I floated out of my body. I could see myself under the water but I wasn't afraid . All of a sudden I started going up a tunnel, and before I could think about it, I found myself in heaven. I know it was heaven because everything was bright and everyone was cheerful.

A nice man asked me if I wanted to stay there. I thought about staying; I really did. But I said 'I want to be with my family.' Then I got to come back.

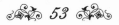

Six-year-old Daniel was struck by a car while riding his bicycle and received a severe head trauma. He was comatose for two weeks. He remembers almost nothing of the accident or of the moments before. He says he remembers taking his bicycle out of the garage and riding down the driveway. His most vivid remembrance is what happened after he was struck:

7

I was standing there watching the doctors load me into the ambulance, when I saw that I was outside my body. My mom was crying and everyone was in a hurry.

When I got to the hospital, I watched the doctors put tubes in me. I looked yucky because I was bloody and bruised.

I then went down a tunnel that was dark. At the end of the tunnel was a bright light. I wasn't sad and I wasn't happy, but I did want to get to the light. When I got to it, I met three men. One was very tall and the other two were short. Behind them was a rainbow bridge that stretched across the sky. They seemed nice, but I was afraid of them anyway.

All of a sudden I was back in my body. I looked down at my feet, and the men were there. Then they disappeared, and I was completely back.

8

I have another story from one of my own patients. When I am wondering about the mysterious nature of the soul and the unknown energy that sparks our lives, I think about this case.

It happened to a boy I'll call Ben. This "boy" is now a 47-year-old policeman, but when he was fourteen, he developed a serious case of rheumatic fever and was hospitalized for weeks at Boston Children's Hospital.

His situation continued to worsen, until one day he began experiencing severe chest pains. They became worse and worse until he could ignore them no longer. He remembers speaking to the nurse and saying that something bad was happening. He saw her run from the room to get a doctor, and then he noticed something strange: He was able to follow her. He floated behind her as she explained the situation to a doctor and then followed them as they ran back into his room to look at his body. He realized that he was looking at his own body, hovering above the whole scene like a dispassionate observer.

... A few seconds earlier he had been in severe pain. Now he was floating painlessly above his body while doctors and nurses began their life-saving cardiac resuscitation.

While he watched what was going on below him, he suddenly felt as though there had been a great increase in his intelligence. He became aware of two Beings of Light, one on either side, who stayed with him as he peacefully watched the frantic scene below. He says that the presence of these beings gave him a sense of peace, love, and understanding. It wasn't as though he 'knew everything,' Ben now says. 'It was more like I suddenly realized that life is a lot more simple than most of us think.'

The doctors were losing Ben, or at least his body. They had tried everything they knew and were now pushing a long needle into his chest to inject his heart with epinephrine. As he watched this desperate procedure, the Beings of Light asked if he wanted to stay on earth or go with them. 'I want to stay,' he said, watching as the doctors waited for the epinephrine to kick in.

The beings left, and Ben watched as the doctors gave up and pulled a sheet over his face. He could hear people talking in the hallway, consoling the doctors and nurses who had just lost their young patient. A student nurse remained at his bedside, softly crying. She had worked with him throughout his long hospitalization, and they had gotten to know each other quite well.

Suddenly, the Beings of Light reappeared and told him he could return to his body. Ben could hardly believe it. He thought he was dead, and from the looks of things, he was. Now the two spirits told him that he could return to his body, a body that had been left for dead by his physicians.

With what felt like a hiccup, Ben was back in his body. He threw the sheet from himself, pulled the needle from his chest, and shouted, 'I'm alive!'

The International Association for Near-Death Studies (IANDS) in Connecticut was founded in 1977 by Dr. Raymond Moody, Dr. Bruce Greyson, Dr. Michael Sabom, and Dr. Kenneth Ring. The purpose of the association is to bring an interdisciplinary approach to the near-death research. It now has hundreds of chapters worldwide.

... In one of these accounts, a four-year-old girl, using a flashlight to go down the cellar stairs, stepped off the edge of the wrong side of the landing and fell to the cement floor far below. At a later age, she described what happened:

[9]

The next thing I was aware of was being up near the ceiling over the foot of the stairs. The light was dim and at first I saw nothing unusual. Then I saw myself lying, face-down, on the cement, over to the side of the stairway. I was a little surprised, but not at all upset at seeing myself that way. I watched and saw that I didn't move at all. After a while, I said to myself, 'I guess I'm dead.' But I felt good! Better than I ever had. I realized I probably wouldn't be going back to my mother, but I wasn't afraid at all. ...

I noticed the dim light growing slowly brighter. The source of light was not in the basement, but far behind and slightly above me. I looked over my shoulder into the most beautiful light imaginable. It seemed to be at the end of a long tunnel which was gradually getting brighter and brighter as more and more of the light entered it. It was yellow-white and brilliant, but not painful to look at even directly. As I turned to face the light with my full 'body,' I felt happier than I ever had before or have since.

Then the light was gone. (And back in my body) I felt groggy and sick, with a terrible headache. I only wanted my mother, and to stop my head from hurting.

End; excerpts quoted from: *Closer to the Light* by Dr. Melvin Morse, 1992.

Dr. Morse is clearly in favour of the belief that in the near-death experience, the person's spirit actually leaves the body. In my estimation, the facts are overwhelmingly supportive of this. Nevertheless, a passionate debate goes on. The *Daily Mail* newspaper for example, ran a series on this subject for one week in 1995 from February 27th to March 2nd. Thursday's headlining statement read: *"...it is an argument that no one can win... The point at issue is life after death — Is there a door to paradise? The questions are simple; the answers eternally elusive."*

At this point, the opinion of a certain skeptic is cited, in which she insists that *"everything about these experiences can be explained by what is happening in the dying brain."* As the article continues however, her argument begins to fall apart, until even Ms Blackmore (the Skeptic) confesses that she has doubts about her own conclusions.

When asked about certain aspects of near-death experiences, her reply is: "I've come up with various answers to that, but I'm afraid all of them have been knocked down. The truth is that I don't really know."

Bringing forward the argument in favour of near-death experiences as being real, the article introduces the following:

Cambridge-trained scientists Dr. Peter Fenwick and his wife Elizabeth are in the opposing corner. They can refute each of Susan Blackmore's arguments and present a convincing counter argument that near-death experiences are indeed a tantalising taste of the afterlife.

'Sue just doesn't have the knowledge,' Dr. Fenwick believes. 'At the Maudsley Hospital where I'm a consultant neuro-psychiatrist, we are dealing all day and every day with people who are confused, disoriented and brain-damaged.'

'What is quite clear is that any disorientation of brain function leads to a disorientation of perception and reduced memory. You can't normally get highly-structured and clearly remembered experiences from a highly damaged or disoriented brain.'

(...)

'So I'm absolutely sure that such experiences are not caused by oxygen shortages, endorphins or anything of that kind...'

Elizabeth Fenwick co-wrote The Truth in the Light, in which more than 300 near-death experiences are described. At the outset, she expected to come to the same conclusions as Susan Blackmore that all could be explained in scientific terms. As Elizabeth is an agnostic, she certainly had no preset religious agenda to fulfill.

Writing the book has turned out to be something of a conversion experience. Elizabeth now believes that there is, in all probability, 'some sort of continuity of soul or spirit after we die.'

(...)

The Fenwicks' views have been given powerful support by the results of a new study of near-death experiences in

Holland. Over a three-year period, distinguished cardiologist Dr. Willem van Lommel and his team studied 345 cases in 11 Dutch hospitals of people who had suffered cardiac arrest and who would have died without resuscitation.

Ten percent recalled a substantial near-death experience, a further eight percent had a less pronounced one. Between one and two years later, the patients were re-interviewed to check whether they were telling the same stories. In virtually every case, they were.

◆　　◆　　◆

The reality of near-death experiences as being true excursions of the spirit outside the body is highlighted by the concept of what is called an autoscopic experience.

There are a number of books and publications which demonstrate this with impeccable documentation. One of these is *Beyond Death's Door* by Maurice Rawlings who comments thus:

[10]

More and more of my patients who are recovering from serious illnesses tell me there is a life after death.

As a cardiologist exposed to critically ill patients in the coronary care units of several hospitals, I have had many opportunities to resuscitate people who have clinically died. I have found that an interview immediately after patients are revived reveals as many bad experiences as good ones.

Before gathering material for this book, I personally regarded most after-death experiences as fantasy of conjecture or imagination. (...) Now I feel assured that there is life after death, and not all of it is good.

The remarkable repetitive sequence of events and parallel experiences in completely unrelated cases seems to exclude the possibility of any coincidence...

Included in case reports (discussed in Rawlings' book) will be some baffling instances of recall of specific events that actually occurred in the confinement of the room during the period of clinical death and complete unconsciousness. The events are so minutely and accurately recounted by the patient as to suggest a spiritual existence outside the body during this period of clinical death.

Dr. Maurice Rawlings

• ◆ ◆

Another book which illustrates this concept is *Recollections of Death* by Dr. Michael B. Sabom who in the Preface to his work writes:

[11]

In my own practice of cardiology over the past five years, I have conducted an extensive investigation into the experiences encountered by persons who have been very close to death. Many of these people, victims of cardiac arrest and other life-threatening crises, recalled a series of extraordinary events that took place while they were unconscious and near death.

[12]

From *Recollections of Death* I give examples:

The following experience was described by a 44-year-old man who had suffered a massive heart attack and cardiac arrest in the intensive care unit during his second hospital day. His resuscitation required multiple electric shocks to the chest. From his vantage point detached from his physical body, he was able to observe carefully and then later to recall, among other things, the movement of the meter needles on the face of the (defibrillator) that delivered the electric shock to his chest. He had never seen a defibrillator in use before.

It was almost like I was detached, standing off to the side and watching it all going on, not being a participant at all but being an uninterested observer... The first thing they did was to put an injection into the IV, the rubber gasket they have there for pushes.

...Then they lifted me up and moved me onto the plywood. That's when Dr. A began to do the pounding on the chest... They had oxygen on me before, one of those little nose tubes, and they took that off and put on a face mask which covers your mouth and nose. It was a type of pressure thing... sort of a soft plastic mask, light green color... I remember them pulling over the cart, the defibrillator, the thing with the paddles on it... It had a meter on the face... It was square and had two needles on there, one fixed and one which moved ... (The needle) seemed to come up rather slowly, really.
(...)

Another 'visual' description of a near-death crisis event, this time a grand mal seizure associated with severe toxemia of pregnancy seventeen years previously, was given by a 37-year-old housewife as if she had been seated in a 'balcony looking down.' According to her, this was the only seizure she had ever witnessed:

I knew something was going to happen... and then I went unconscious... and I was looking down and could see myself going into convulsions, and I was starting to fall out of bed, and the girl in the next bed screaming for the nurses... The nurse caught me and put me back and by then there were two other nurses there and one came back almost immediately with a tongue depressor on my tongue. And they got the sides up on the bed and they called the doctor... It was a feeling of height, great distance, a light feeling, like being up in a balcony looking down and watching all this and feeling very detached as though I was watching someone else, like you might watch a movie... It was a very calm, relaxed feeling, a feeling of well-being if anything... Everything was clearly seen, like watching television... It looked very ugly to me to see my body thrashing around on the bed... and the way I was jerking around... was very frightening to the girl in the other bed... The convulsion didn't last very long and the next thing I was aware of, I don't know how the change took place, but I woke up the next morning and I was back to me again.

A 60-year-old Ohio housewife suffered a cardiac arrest while hospitalized in January 1978 and experienced the following:

I had left my body and was to the side in sort of like a tube... They called the express team and I could see them coming in and all the doctors and nurses and all the confusion... They were punching my chest, putting IVs in me; they were all rushing around... Some of the others were packing my belongings because they were going to take me up to ICU (the intensive care unit)... I could see their faces and the backs of the ones who had their backs to me... I could see the little needle they were putting in my hand. Something about the blood gases... I could see my face very clearly, and they were lifting my eyelids. They were pulling my eyelids up to look to see where my eyes were, I guess. That's the only way I can explain it. Then they were feeling around my neck where the pulse is. Most of the time it was just this pushing on my chest... They had the breathing machine and a cart with a whole bunch of stuff on it, but I don't know what all those things were... I had seen them grabbing all this stuff out of my locker, which was right at the foot of my bed. I could see around the backs of these people, and I saw this one girl grabbing everything because the doctor had said, 'We're going to have to get her up to ICU.' She was grabbing everything out of my drawer and dumping it into bags and suitcases. When I came to, everything was labeled with my name on it, to go upstairs...

A 50-year-old real estate broker described the events of his cardiac arrest and NDE, which occurred in the intensive care unit of a Florida hospital in January 1975:

Then I got my chest pain and passed out. I don't remember anything for a while, and the next thing I remember I was hanging on the ceiling looking down on them working on my body... She (the nurse) put a needle in there and was shooting it into the IV... It looked like he (the doctor) had one hand on my chest and he kept hitting it real hard. I could see the bed moving up and down... It (the cardiac monitor) wasn't running at that time. The red light was on and there was a line across. Instead of running up and down like, there was just a line across. It seems that whatever they had done got the monitor running again. That's when I got back in bed.

These people who had observed their own physical bodies from this 'out-of-body' state described a total absence of pain even while they underwent painful medical procedures without anesthesia.

End Quote; *Recollections of Death*, by Dr. Micheal B. Sabom

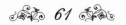

The foregoing excerpts are typical cases of people who were totally unconscious or even clinically dead during the time of the events they describe. These however, are merely a small fraction of such cases given in the said works, many of which go into complex medical details.

One of the objectives of this chapter is to demonstrate in some degree the phenomenal number of well documented NDE cases which are extant in the world today. Among the many published works in this field of study, *Return from Death* by Margot Grey contains a superb collection of experiences, from which I give the following excerpts:

A woman recalled her heart attack as follows: [13]

I was in the intensive care unit of Worthing hospital. During the early hours, I found myself suspended above my body looking down at myself.

I heard and saw two doctors and a nurse running towards the bed and heard them say 'quick, quick'.

I am sure I had died.

A man who had been in hospital undergoing treatment for leukemia also referred to this sense of spiritual identity:

I became aware of my spirit, or whatever you want to call it, being up in a corner of the room and looking down on my body with doctors and nurses, and all the people and hospital paraphernalia being brought into the room and piled o n my chest and so forth. I could not feel any of this at the time it was happening, but I was like a spectator looking down on this from up in the corner of the room. I didn't have any regrets or anything, it just felt kind of strange.

Another aspect of this phase of the 'core experience' that occurs frequently enough to warrant a special mention is the feature of illumination. A man who nearly died following an operation for a double strangulated hernia recalled:

I was suddenly conscious of all around me, although I couldn't move or speak. Then I was aware of looking down on my bed and seeing myself, a shriveled old man, a pitiful lifeless being. I was next aware of indescribably beautiful colours and a brightness most intense.

A second hyperventilation case who had been treated in the cardiac ward of Charing Cross Hospital observed:

I suddenly became aware I was floating above myself and all the fear and panic seemed to go. I was calm and everything was very bright. I felt peaceful and warm. It was really beautiful.

A man related the ensuing experience following a cardiac arrest:

They took me into the emergency room and I guess they started working on me at this point. I guess at this point I left my body as I seemed to be up above the room. I had never been in this room before, I was unconscious when they brought me in. I was above the room in a corner and I could see the doctors, as clear as a bell, working on me.... One said, 'I think he's gone, let's try some electrical thing'; I don't know what it was. They put a pad on me and then they put these electrical things on me and said something about mega volts. They must have started up my heart or something of that sort, I knew nothing more until I opened my eyes and I was in the intensive care unit. Now I looked up and there's these guys I've never seen before and they were the same people I had seen while I was unconscious. About a month later I wanted to make sure this was not a hallucination something of that sort and I went back to this hospital and I asked the nurse to show me this room which I had never seen in my life before and I walked in there and I knew where everything was. It was all there, the table, the lights, the cabinet, everything, like I remembered.

Another source of meticulously documented NDE phenomena is a volume of research entitled *The Near Death Experience: Problems, Prospects, Perspectives.*

Out of many experiences which are analysed in the work, we shall include the account of a woman who experienced the following in the course of an operation:

[14]

(She remembers hearing someone say that they were going to do a 'cut down' on her and then) I remember being above the bed - I was not in the bed anymore - looking down on me lying in the bed and I remember saying to myself, 'I don't want you to do a cut down on me.'

...I know (from what she was told afterward) that the doctors worked on me for many hours. And I remember being first above my body and then I remember being in, like a valley. And this valley reminded me of what I think of as the valley of the shadow of death. I also remember it being a very pretty valley. Very pleasant. And I felt very calm at that point. I met a person in this valley. And this person - I realized it later on - was my (deceased) grandfather, who I had never met. (She then describes how she was able to identify him after talking to her grandmother about it.) I remember my grandfather saying to me, "Helen, don't give up. You're still needed. I'm not ready for you yet." It was that kind of thing. And then I remember music. (Can you describe it for me?) It was kind of like church music, in a sense. Spiritual music. (Was there singing? Were there musical instruments that you could identify?) No. No... it had... somehow a sad quality about it. A very awesome quality to it.

❖   ❖   ❖

By a comparative study of information found in experiences such as have been listed in this chapter, a very limited yet extraordinary glimpse of what takes place after death unfolds to our perceptions. Acknowledging this, it is essential to bear in mind that this collective glimpse of an existence beyond the threshold of death — extraordinary as it is — is only a minimal view. It is superfluous to assume that we know much about the spirit world from these momentary excursions.

We have observed the consistent statements of people that immediately upon finding themselves out of the body, they feel a tremendous sense of peace, and complete cessation of physical pain or stress insomuch that they are desirous to remain in their disembodied condition — regardless of leaving loved ones behind in mortality. Having noted this, it is requisite to develop our consideration a step further.

The initial satisfaction of being out of the body which has been described to us, must be regarded as a temporary effect resulting from the great contrast between the physical pains endured in mortality and the immediate release from all such things when departure from the body occurs.

We must take into account that these spiritual excursions are all from people whose time out of the body was relatively short. Those who stay on the other side for greater lengths of time are also those who do not come back to tell of it. Someone who has been thus discarnate for a much longer time, would undoubtedly have a different perspective to offer, for after the initial thrill of soaring beyond one's body has subsided, other realities will inevitably come to view. A demonstration of this may be drawn from George Ritchie's experience in which he saw many spirits in terrible distress as tormented prisoners of their own base nature. (See: *Return From Tomorrow*, by George Ritchie, 1978, pp.59-65.)

Before birth into this life, we had already existed for an unknown expanse of time as spirits. To simply return to that state, though refreshing at first, puts us to some extent right back where we started.

In the pre-mortal existence, as the time approached for us to gain a physical body, we were undoubtedly quite anxious for that to come about. And now after mortality, when our spirits have been without the body for an extended period, we shall feel an acute sense of longing to be whole. The only solution to our incompleteness will be in the resurrection and reunion of our body and spirit.

❖   ❖   ❖

The Spirit and the Body

This chapter, on near-death experiences is designed simply to demonstrate the remarkable spectrum and plenitude of such incidents. We do not propose this to suffice as a comprehensive scientific study. The subject of near-death experiences, as well as "death-bed visions" discussed in the ensuing chapter, have been much more fully addressed in other publications, a few of which are listed below:

References

1- Return From Death; Margot Grey: 1985. (p.37)

2- " " " (p.35)

3- Beyond Death's Door; Maurice Rawlings: 1978. (pp. 80-81)

4- Transformed By the Light; Dr Melvin Morse: 1992

5- Closer to the Light; Dr. Melvin Morse: 1992. (p.5)

6- " " " (pp. 36-37)

7- " " " (p.46)

8- " " " (pp. 128-30)

9- " " " (pp.135-36)

10- Beyond Death's Door; Maurice Rawlings: 1978. (p.17 & p.xi-xiii)

11- Recollections of Death: Dr. Michael B. Sabom M.D. 1982. (p.xii)

12- " " " (p.p. 28-31)

13- Return From Death: Margot Grey: (pp. 34-38)

14- The Near-Death Experience: Problems, Prospects, and Perspectives: Edited by Bruce Greyson M.D. Assistant Professor of Psychiatry. Chief Psychiatric Emergency Service University of Michigan Medical Center. AnArbor, Michigan. And Charles P. Flynn Ph.D. Associate Professor of Sociology Miami University, Oxford OHIO 1984. (p.42)

The Transition

Whenever I hear someone express feelings of fear with regards to death, it comes as, almost a surprise. For I easily forget that indeed, many people are afraid of dying. Many are consumed with apprehension, uncertainty and anxiety regarding this giant step into the unknown.

For me, it appears as a transition from this mortal period back to the eternal road from which we came. I do not merely *believe* in life beyond the threshold called death. I know, that we all will continue beyond the cessation of this tabernacle of clay in which we live.

The clarity with which the concept of the NDE and life after death resides in my mind is the motivation behind a number of songs I have composed on the subject.

One in particular, a fourteen minute composition entitled *"The Transition,"* paints a picture both lyrically and instrumentally of this phenomenon. The lyrics of which, I give here:

When you must endure the day
when a loved one has died
it can bring you down and tear you up inside
When it was your loved one
who has gone away
and left you here to stay

Sailing into silence
is the way that death might seem

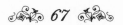

but it's not the way you'll find it
when your life becomes a dream

Death is not like dying
It's more like being born
but you leave behind a worn out shell
like a glove that has been torn
Just like your loved ones
you will see the light
when your spirit takes flight
and eternity comes to view

Death is a transition
not the final end
Never say die again

When you die
your everlasting soul will start to rise
and looking down, you'll watch your loved ones
as they hope and pray and cry
over you
but there's nothing that they can do

Many have gone before us here
and come back with
amazing stories
The meaning of life becomes so clear
to all who behold, the unseen glory

This short life is not the end
the spirit moves on
when you're
dead

I see the golden light
the earth begins to fade below me
the life I knew must now get left
behind

It all becomes so clear now
we will endure and last forever
I see that life extends beyond the grave

I made the transition
when my heart stopped beating in time
and I can't explain the way I feel

I thought I saw the falling stars
that are men who didn't believe
that a soul lives on to pay for all its greed

And the moment was endless

I was in motion
with one foot in the grave
now I'm living again
and I know I'll never be the same
never gonna be the same

I'm never gonna be the same

❖   ❖   ❖   ❖   ❖

Lyrics and Music: Shane O'Brien, © 1996
Available on the album: *The Well of Souls*
from OMEGA RECORDS.

Death-Bed Visions

Another aspect of the near-death experience deserving of notice, is something which comes under the subject of "death-bed visions."

There have been occasions when family members, or medical staff etc., administering to someone in his last moments have seen the patient begin mouthing words while looking up into blank space in the room. Sometimes a dying person will lift up a hand as if reaching out to someone, or call out the name of a departed relative. The significance of these actions has often been overlooked.

Gathering information on the subject, we have grounds to understand that at the time of death, at least in some cases, beings from the spirit world such as deceased relatives come to escort the person who is about to leave mortality. Moreover, the vision of the dying one may open, apparently, in such a manner that he can see things of the spirit.

In the course of my inquiries, cases were documented in which people have noted that just before passing away, the dying person became remarkably confident in the sweetness of the step which he was about to take.

With an expression of joy and peacefulness these individuals have uttered such things as *"I'm in a garden!" "Flowers are everywhere! It's beautiful,"* and in the next breath the patient dies.

Again, statements such as this coming from a dying person are commonly dismissed as incoherent babblings. The truth of the matter however, is far more inspiring than that. The concept we are dealing with is thought provokingly introduced in a book entitled; *Death Bed Visions* by Sir William Barrett, physicist at the Royal College of Science in Dublin. He began investigating death-bed visions in the 1920's after his wife, an obstetrician witnessed a peculiar incident as follows:

On the night of January 12, 1924, Lady Barrett delivered the baby of a woman named Doris. After the difficult birth, as the woman lay dying, she looked toward one part of the room with a radiant smile. "Oh, lovely, lovely," she said. When asked what was lovely, Doris replied, "What I see." She spoke in a low, intense voice. "Lovely brightness-wonderful beings."

Then, Lady Barrett reported, Doris seemed to focus on one spot in the room and cried out, "Why, it's Father! Oh, he's so glad I'm coming; he is so glad..."

Doris's baby was brought for her to see. She looked at it with concern, and then said, "Do you think I ought to stay for baby's sake?" ...Speaking presumably to her father, she said, "I am coming" and then, puzzled, commented to the bystanders, "He has Vida with him."

The woman died shortly afterward. Aside from the sheer intensity of Doris's feelings and speech, what made the greatest impression on Sir William and Lady Barrett was the fact that Vida, Doris's sister, had died three weeks earlier, but Doris had not been told because of her precarious health. Doris, it seems, had a vision of someone she could not have expected to see.

This account and others appear in the book, *At the Hour of Death* by Dr. Karlis Osis (1986), which covers the subject thoroughly and scientifically. The results of extensive surveys and studies are compiled therein, demonstrating that death-bed visions are not mere hallucinations. The work does not neglect the fact that in many cases, a dying patient who *sees things* may indeed be having delusions. The difference between the *imagined* and the *real* visions must be acknowledged and borne in mind if there is to be a coherent understanding of the intrinsic value of this concept.

At the time William Barrett conducted his observations the prevailing medical belief was that when a dying patient said or did anything abnormal, it was due to delirium or hallucinations.

Barrett pointed out that death-bed visions often occur when the patient's mind is clear and rational. Furthermore, he observed that in multiple instances, dying children had spoken of seeing angels without wings. If their visions were hallucinations, Barrett felt, they would have been likely to conform to popular stereotypes.

In the account of a death-bed vision, published in 1864 in booklet form, a mother related that her daughter was able to see her brother who had died seven months previously, while she, herself, could not:

> I was sitting beside her bed, her hand clasped in mine. Looking up so wistfully at me, she said, 'dear momma, I do wish you could see Allie (a son who had died seven months previously); he's standing beside you!'
>
> Involuntarily I looked around, but Daisy continued, 'He says you cannot see him because your spirit eyes are closed, but that I can, because my body only holds my spirit, as it were, by a thread of life.'
>
> 'Dear mom, I do wish you could see Allie'... I then asked her further, 'Daisy, how does Allie appear to you? Does he seem to wear clothes?' She answered, 'Oh no, not clothes such as we wear. There seems to be about him a white, beautiful something, so fine and thin and glistening, and oh, so white, and yet there is not a fold, or a sign of a thread in it, so it cannot be cloth. But it makes him look so lovely.' Her father then quoted from the Psalmist: 'He is clothed with light as a garment.' 'Oh yes, that's it,' she replied.

* The Return from Silence; D. Scott Rogo, 1989, p.48

Several incidents relating to our present focus have been reported to me by those who actually witnessed the events.

Mrs. Winnie Willmott, a dear friend of mine and indeed of many people, was at the bedside of her young niece Doris when the girl died. "Doris," Winnie recalls, "was a beautiful little blonde whom everyone adored." Sadly, in 1930, when Doris was only four years old, her mother passed away. Four years later, Doris fell off a vaulting horse at school and sustained a serious injury. She was taken to Whittington Hospital at Highgate in North London. After a few days, her condition worsened. Family members were notified who then came to be with Doris.

On December 29, about ten concerned individuals, including Doris's Father, step-Mother and aunt Winnie were gathered around her bedside. Doris, now critically ill, suddenly sat up in bed. Her face lit up with joy and looking directly up towards the corner of the ceiling she called out *"Mummy! Mummy!"* and then died straight after.

Poignant questions may be raised here. Why did Doris suddenly raise up with an expression of joy, and acknowledge a personage in the upper part of the room, whom she identified as her mother who had died four years earlier?

Another case may be cited from the experience of Mrs. Glenister, a friend who at my request, kindly provided the following account:

> Uncle George, in his early eighties, was in hospital terminally ill with cancer. He had no children of his own so my brothers and I were taking it in turns to sit with him.
>
> On the 31st of January 1990 my eldest brother telephoned me early in the morning and asked if I could exchange with him and go in to be with Uncle George in the morning instead of in the afternoon. This I agreed to do.
>
> I set off for the hospital, a forty minute drive, and when I arrived Uncle George was pleased to see me. He was propped up in bed in the sitting position. I held his hand in both of mine and asked him how he was feeling. We sat quietly like this for some time. Then he asked "am I in heaven?" I replied, "not yet." Then he said "I can see Angels."
>
> After a while I noticed the pulse in his neck becoming weaker and weaker and it finally stopped. Uncle George still had his eyes open.

One man in particular, Dean, shared with me the details of when his father passed away. Dean was working in London at the time and received a phone call from his mother bearing the unfortunate news that his Father, whom he admired greatly, was dying.

Dean immediately set off for Newcastle and arrived just in time to see John Orlando Brandon Chambers for the last time in mortality.

Notwithstanding the elderly Mr. Chambers being very weak and sedate in these final moments, Dean recalls that just before dying, he suddenly perked up, his eyes opened and now fully alert and awake, he exclaimed with joy: *"It's beautiful over there!"* and then expired.

Dean holds the noble life of his father in high esteem. From the foregoing experience it appears that a view of the place to which Mr. Chambers was now going — the spirit paradise — opened unto him.

❖   ❖   ❖

Of additional interest, is the concept epitomized in the following detail from *Otherworld Journeys* by Carol Zeleski:
"A doctor by the name of Andrew Jackson Davis witnessed the spirit of one of his patients as it departed from her body. In his account, Dr. Davis marvels that her spirit personage was identical to her physical body, however she looked healthy and youthful in appearance which transcended her present physical condition."

Upon careful surveys and due consideration, we may ascertain that rare incidents do occur in which immediately or soon after death, the spirit of the deceased is seen by a relative, a loved one, or perhaps a doctor or nurse as in the above instance. The reasons for these fleeting glimpses of a departing spirit are of course varied and ambiguous. Often though, the reason has to do with last goodbyes and reconciliation with those being left behind in mortality.

A sublime example of this comes from a dear friend of mine whose wife died through an unfortunate turn of events. The situation was heart-wrenching for those involved, therefore while my friend is willing to permit me to relate his experience

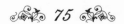

here, in consideration for the sensitivity and privacy of the issue I prefer to use substitute names. The details however are given as they happened.

Departure of a Loved One

Terry and Julia were in their 2nd year of marriage. Adding to the joy they shared as a young man and wife was the birth of their first child, James.

Sadly, an ominous turn occurred when Julia began to show signs of post-natal depression. Over the next few months things continued to get worse to the point that in August, Julia was hospitalised. She was suffering from "peripheral psychosis" in consequence of the post-natal syndrome.

On her second night in hospital, a fly got into a smoke detector—probably attracted by an LED—and triggered the alarm system in the psychiatric ward where she was staying. Julia was sound asleep at the time the alarm went off, which threw her into a panic. She jumped up and ran frantically across the beds and straight through the large plate window of her room on the upper floor of the hospital.

Severely injured and unconscious, Julia was carefully lifted from the pavement and taken by ambulance to the intensive care unit which was some distance from the psychiatric wing. Terry was contacted immediately. Arriving at the hospital he rushed through the doors asking to see his wife—but was restrained by hospital staff who tried to make him understand that for the moment, her condition was too critical for such a visit. The emergency medical staff were working against the clock to save her.

Terry was ushered into a waiting room and offered gallons of coffee—which he patiently refused every time. He begged to see his wife but was still not permitted. After what seemed like an eternity, a doctor from intensive care came in saying "...we would like you to be nearer to where your wife is." Bitter emotions of uncertainty seized his breast as Terry was led down the long hospital corridors. However, the doctor had discussed with him that after her recovery, Julia would need care and assistance, which Terry interpreted to mean that his wife was recovering and would at least survive.

Arriving at a staff-room in ICU, Terry was asked to wait. He sat down, trembling and distraught. About ten minutes had passed when as he sat leaning forward with face in hands, just looking at the floor, he suddenly saw Julia coming through the doorway. It is an enigma that he was able to see this, while not actually facing that direction. As Julia approached, he immediately saw that she was a spirit, not possessing the tangible form in which he had always known her. Julia normally wore glasses, but now did not appear to need them. Her apparel was not of this earth. Terry recalls clearly the beautiful and surreal way that her gown rippled and waved as she moved.

She came to him and said *"I'm sorry Terry, but I just can't go back in that body."* And then she was gone. About five minutes later, a doctor came in and reticently said to Terry; "with sincere apologies and regrets, I have to tell you that your wife has just passed away."

❖   ❖   ❖

When my friend told me of his experience, one particular detail came up which I had heard before in several other interviews, but had not given much attention. It became apparent that it was while he sat with his head down, looking at the floor that he saw Julia. I then commented, "so you didn't exactly see her, you pictured her in your mind." His reply was clear and direct: "I *saw* her. I don't know how, because it wasn't with my natural eyes — like we normally see — but nevertheless, I saw her. It was not an imagined thing."

The reason this detail held new significance for me is that hearing it in previous instances, always made me feel that the apparition must have been imagined, because it was not directly seen through the eyes of flesh. It stands to reason though, that on those rare, brief occasions when a person is able to actually *see* a spirit, it is not necessarily the eyes of flesh which have caught this glimpse, but the eyes of a person's spirit. This all becomes thoroughly complicated however, as speculative discussions such as this simply give no answers but raise a score of questions.

I certainly don't have the answers, but what I do know, is the integrity of the individual who had this experience. A man of a sounder mind, there is not. In his own successful company his line of work involves the design, programming and implimentation of complex industrial computerised systems which form the interface between machinery and centralised computerisation.

Quite simply, he says that while waiting at the hospital for news concerning his wife's condition, her spirit approached and essentially bade him farewell. I believe it is so.

To his story, I could add several more from personal friends and acquaintances who have received a farewell visit from a departed loved one. But frankly, what good would that do? We can tell these experiences till the cows come home and still not grasp the impact and reality involved. Part of this lack of confidence in such stories is well placed, because many times, they are simply not true. People do imagine and fabricate such tales.

The justifiable skepticism with which we are prone to receive things of this nature renders it for the most part, futile to share the experiences. The example cited above is here because I have no doubt of its veracity and it serves as a model representation of this concept.

To bring this chapter to its conclusion, I shall give one additional situation:

Midge, an acquaintance of mine related to me the touching account of Lisa, a thirteen-year-old girl who was dying of cancer. In 1990, Midge had cancer herself, thus she was a patient at Guys Hospital in London.

While waiting for an operation, Midge shared the same Ward with Lisa.

Midge felt great compassion for Lisa, because even though both of them had cancer, Midge was likely to survive after her operation. Lisa on the other hand was terminally ill — and preparations were being made to move her to a hospice, where she would die.

Searching for the right words, Midge sat at Lisa's bedside, wishing her good luck. The girl, though very weak, replied gleefully saying *"Oh I'm very excited... it's my birthday today!"* *"How old are you?"* Midge asked. *"I'm thirteen! ...I'm going with my brother in three weeks!"*

Midge was puzzled. She really didn't think this little girl would be going *anywhere* in three weeks, and politely replied: *"You're going on holiday somewhere —somewhere nice?"*

"No my brother died four years ago."

"How old was your brother?"

"He was twenty-one."

"How did your brother die?"

"In a car accident."

The implications of Lisa's statements were suddenly very clear. But of course Midge didn't know what to think. She didn't know what to say either. She sat silently with the girl for a time, then finally asked, *"Where are you going?"* Lisa either misinterpreted the question, or changed the subject by answering; *"To the hospice."* At that time Midge did not know exactly what a hospice was, thus replied, *"What is a hospice?"* Lisa answered directly: *"A place to die."*

Midge asked sensitively; *"How can you go with your brother, if he died four years ago?"*

"He's been to see me here twice. I didn't tell the Nurse, because she wouldn't believe it — but Robert says he'll be here to take me with him when it's time. And I know it will be wonderful. And I will be well again."

Midge still didn't know what to think, but she marveled at the peace and confidence this girl had, knowing that she was simply waiting to die.

Later that afternoon, the nurses took Lisa away for transferral to the hospice. Midge never saw her again, but will never forget the girl.

From here, we could go on listing numerous further incidents of this type. To detail those accounts here though, would merely be repetitive of the examples already given.

In light of the extensive and well documented studies in this field which have been carried out and published in other works, it becomes pragmatic to acknowledge this as a tangible demonstration of the reality that beyond our normal visual capacities here, is the spirit world, to which we also shall go.

War in Heaven

I remember the summer of '95'. In June, two children, a boy and a girl ages eight and nine, were found dead in a field. They had been murdered. Before the end of the month the news rang out with the story of a ten-year-old boy, in a different part of the country, the same thing.

July. A man was arrested in London for the sexual assault and strangling of an eleven-year-old boy. Still in July, a teenage girl was found by the motor-way, murdered. On the other end of the age spectrum, a seventy-year-old woman was at home one evening, minding her own business, when an intruder broke in, killed her, and stole away with the meagre amount of cash she possessed. Even at the moment of writing this, the television news is giving a report on two men, paedophiles, who abducted a four-year-old boy. They committed "horrible crimes" upon the child and then murdered him. Shall I go on? I think not. The mere mention of such acts is distressing and even distasteful.

Not only do we have the atrocity of murder to taint our existence in this world, but an endless spectrum of cruelties and appalling deeds. On a world-wide scale, the 'summer of 95' is of course no different from the spring of '95', and of '94' and so on. Basically all year round, year after year, a continual series of atrocities unfolds.

What is this phenomenon by which some people are disposed to inflict such great misery and pain upon others? In fine, we see in these things a manifestation of evil.

When the face and personality of evil is unveiled, we see that it is vicious. Void of compassion, evil will attack and devour innocence without provocation. It revels in darkness. Rooted in the heart of evil is hatred, anger, contention, selfishness and bitterness. Evil seeks to cheat and rob others of what they have worked to achieve. Evil has no regard for truth but will practice and promulgate deceit.

When we compare all of these characteristics with the statements of people who, through the experience of an NDE, have seen a glimpse of the world of purity and light beyond this mortality, we find that evil has no place nor power there. Many experiencers have commented upon the beautiful brilliant light which permeates and fills that realm. With great consistency, people have marvelled that in the presence of this light, their souls were filled with happiness and joy. When faced with glory such as this, evil will be much the same as the mythical vampire who cannot bear the sunlight, but scrambles to hide from it in dark recesses. Unlike the everlasting peace and happiness which people have experienced in the realm righteous spirits, when any one of us is in the presence of pervading evil, the overwhelming feelings of our spirit are despair, anxiety, sadness and fear.

People have also discovered that the very essence of thought and communication in the spiritual realm of light is bound in truth. What you really are deep down inside shows out. Your intents and desires are manifest. In an environment like this, evil will flee in shame.

The presence of evil in this earth originates from the rebellion led by Lucifer before the world was populated. The following details from Revelations Chapter 12, convey the basis of this:

> And there was war in heaven: Michael and his angels fought against the dragon; and the dragon fought and his angels, And prevailed not; neither was their place found any more in heaven. And the great dragon was cast out, that old serpent, called the Devil, and Satan, which deceiveth the whole world: he was cast out into the earth, and his angels were cast out with him.

In Revelations 12:4 we find the principal New Testament reference to the fact that one third of the spirits in the pre-mortal existence were drawn away by Lucifer at this time, and sent into the earth; "and his tail drew the third part of the stars of heaven, and did cast them to the earth." This point is stated more clearly in the book of Doctrine and Covenants, Section 29, which says that the devil "rebelled" against God "and also a third part of the hosts of heaven turned he away... and thus came the devil and his angels." (29: 36-37)

Quite simply, in the pre-earth existence of the spirit children of the Eternal Heavenly Father, one spirit in particular who held a high position of seniority — if we may call it such — led a rebellion against the Father and also against Christ.

This leader, Lucifer by name, was evil in himself and lusted after glory, power, and dominion which was not in harmony with the ways of righteousness. He succeeded in deceiving many spirits — who, being cast out of heaven, have remained here on earth to this day. While this may be difficult for some people to believe, there really is no shortage of visible evidence of the actual presence and influence of these unseen beings.

In heaven, Lucifer coveted the position of Christ and desired to usurp the throne of God, yet really had no power to accomplish this. On the earth however, where the children of God would enter mortality, where God's power and presence must remain behind a curtain as it were, this viper and his angels could run and rage, having a substantial degree of power and influence. According to the scriptures, Satan thought that from down here he would be able to destroy the work of God and build up his own kingdom. To some extent he is succeeding at this. The Adversary now leads millions of the Father's children astray and has done so for generations, influencing men and women to commit manifold offences.

There are some in this world who are foolish enough to even seek after Satan to worship and make pacts with him. Their souls they will trade, for worldly success and luxuries which he promises them. Therefore in this context, at the end of the world, the Devil will have expanded his kingdom and taken possession of the souls of those in this life who made a specific effort to place themselves within his grasp.

As previously stated, it is revealed in the scriptures that one third of the spirits in the pre-earth heaven followed Lucifer and were cast out, into the earth. The implications of this are staggering considering the billions of people that are on the earth today. It is not easy to fathom just how great this number is. As of 1990, the population of Asia was above 3 Billion. Europe was over 500 million, North America over 400 million, South America 300 million and the list goes on. Furthermore, consider that two hundred years ago it was an entirely different generation which inhabited the Earth. Two hundred years before that another generation, and so forth back to the time of Noah, and before that time, the same again (However it is pertinent to add that in past ages, the world population was much lower than as seen in the present century.) In any case, add all these generations together, imagine a half of those billions of souls and this is a rough idea of the number of evil spirits, pawns of Lucifer which are extant in the earth today. Every living person on this planet must be outnumbered by evil spirits by at least ten to one.

The occupation of this great unseen army is to influence the living in a negative manner. To deceive and bring us under subjection to the will of the Devil. Each of us has a personal responsibility to eschew evil and not allow ourselves to become servants and slaves of the Adversary.

Our position is precarious — in the midst of a war. At present, the war which rages between good and evil, darkness and light, truth and falsehood, is merely an extension of the war which began in the pre-mortal existence. Through yielding to the enticings of the forces of evil, we face a very real risk of becoming casualties suffering spiritual death, becoming POW's of Lucifer.

Moreover, when Satan and his angels rejected the plan of the Father, they forfeited the opportunity of being "added upon" in terms of gaining a physical body. This sets the stage for a rather unpleasant prospect. As this incorporeal, innumerable, un-holy host goes to and fro in the earth, observing and endeavouring to meddle in the affairs of men, a most passionate wish harboured in the mind of each one of them, is to possess a body. Envious of the physical aspect we have, they desiderate the experience, the thrills, frills, power and influence which a body can endow.

A demonstration of this is recorded in the New Testament, wherein Jesus encountered a man whose name is given as "Legion: because many devils were entered into him." At the prospect of being cast out of this man's body, the spirits begged to be sent into a nearby herd of swine rather than into nothing. (Mark 5:8-13 & Luke 8:30-34)

What a perfectly horrible thought, to consider that an unseen, incomprehensible host of evil spirits is waiting, watching, moment by moment seeking the opportunity to pounce on us — and experience life by residing as a parasite in our body. In which case, the propensities and influence of the self-appointed guests would cause a perpetual cycle of misery and disappointment.

Through demonic possession the Devil destroys and wastes many peoples lives. One way for example, is to get them thrown into prison by influencing the person to commit crimes which end up in convictions. Once there, the devils possessing bodies are quite at home in a vile environment where hatred, anger, and debauchery reign. Many people who end up wasting away in prison can to some degree thank their friend the Devil by whom they have been led.

A vivid scene of the readiness of disembodied spirits to enter the bodies of the living is given in the written account of George Ritchie, whose near-death experience carried him through a superlative excursion and vision of the spirit world, which exists as if in another dimension right here in our midst:

> Gradually I began to notice something else. All of the living people we (George Ritchie and his spirit guide), were watching were surrounded by a faint luminous glow, almost like an electrical field over the surface of their bodies. This luminosity moved as they moved, like a second skin make out of pale, scarcely visible light.
>
> At first I thought it must be reflected brightness from the Person (the being of light) at my side. But the buildings we entered gave off no reflection, neither did inanimate objects. And then I realized that the non-physical beings didn't either. My own unsolid body, I now saw, was without this glowing sheath.
>
> At this point the Light drew me inside a dingy bar and grill near what looked like a large naval base. A crowd of

people, many of them sailors, lined the bar three deep, while others jammed wooden booths along the wall. Though a few were drinking beer, most of them seemed to be belting whiskies as fast as the two perspiring bartenders could pour them.

Then I noticed a striking thing. A number of the men standing at the bar seemed unable to lift their drinks to their lips. Over and over I watched them clutch at their shot glasses, hands passing through the solid tumblers, through the heavy wooden counter top, through the very arms and bodies of the drinkers around them.

And these men, every one of them, lacked the aureole of light that surrounded the others.

Then, the cocoon of light must be a property of physical bodies only. The dead, we who had lost our solidness, had lost this "second skin" as well. And it was obvious that these living people, the light-surrounded ones, the ones actually drinking, talking and jostling each other, could neither see the desperately thirsty disembodied beings among them, nor feel their frantic pushing to get at those glasses. Though it was also clear to me, watching, that the non-solid people could both see and hear each other. Furious quarrels were constantly breaking out among them over glasses that none could actually get to his lips.

I thought I had seen heavy drinking at fraternity parties in Richmond, but the way civilians and servicemen at this bar were going at it beat everything. I watched one young sailor rise unsteadily from a stool, take two or three steps, and sag heavily to the floor. Two of his buddies stooped down and started dragging him away from the crush.

But that was not what I was looking at. I was staring in amazement as the bright cocoon around the unconscious sailor simply opened up. It parted at the very crown of his head and began peeling away from his head, his shoulders. Instantly, quicker than I'd ever seen anyone move, one of the insubstantial beings who had

had been standing near him at the bar was on top of him. He had been hovering like a thirsty shadow at the sailor's side, greedily following every swallow the young man made. Now he seemed to spring at him like a beast of prey.

In the next instant, to my utter mystification, the springing figure had vanished. It all happened even before the two men had dragged their unconscious friend from under the feet of those at the bar. One minute I'd distinctly seen two individuals, but by the time they propped the sailor against the wall, there was only one.

Twice more, as I stared, stupefied, the identical scene was repeated. A man passed out, a crack swiftly opened in the aureole round him, one of the non-solid people vanished as he hurled himself at that opening, almost as if he had scrambled inside the other man.

Was that covering of light some kind of shield, then? Was it a protection against... against disembodied beings like myself? Presumably these substance-less creatures had once had solid bodies, as I myself had had. Suppose that when they had been in these bodies they had developed a dependence on alcohol that went beyond the physical. That became mental. Spiritual, even. Then when they lost that body, except when they could briefly take possession of another one, they would be cut off for all eternity from the thing they could never stop craving.

An eternity like that? The thought sent a chill shuddering through me. Surely that would be a form of hell. I had always thought of hell, when I thought of it at all, as a fiery place somewhere beneath the earth where evil men like Hitler would burn forever, but what if one level of hell existed right here on the surface - unseen and unsuspected by the living people occupying the same space. What if it meant remaining on earth but never again able to make contact with it. I thought of that (departed) mother whose son couldn't hear her. The (departed) woman who wanted that cigarette. I thought of myself, caring only about getting to Richmond, unable to make anyone see me or help me. To want most, to

burn with most desire, where you were most powerless -
that would be hell indeed. (...)

A further description of the Hell which George Ritchie
witnessed involves the seeing of many spirits, the wicked souls
of men who had passed on from mortality, who yet retained all
the personality traits, passions and desires which had ruled and
virtually taken possession of them while in the flesh.
He saw fierce contentions prevailing among these spirits as
they would frantically attack each other in vain:

> Although they appeared to be literally on top of each
> other, it was as though each man was boxing the air; I
> realized that of course, having no substance, they could
> not actually touch one another. They could not kill,
> though they clearly wanted to, because their intended
> victims were already dead, and so they hurled
> themselves at each other in a frenzy of impotent rage.
>
> If I suspected before that I was seeing hell, now I was
> sure of it. Up to this moment the misery I had watched
> consisted in being chained to a physical world of which
> we were no longer part. Now I saw that there were other
> kinds of chains. Here were no solid objects or people to
> enthral the soul. These creatures seemed locked into
> habits of mind and emotion, into hatred, lust and
> destructive thought-patterns.
>
> Even more hideous than the bites and kicks they
> exchanged, were the sexual abuses many were performing
> in feverish pantomime. Perversions I had never dreamed
> of were being vainly attempted all around us. It was
> impossible to tell if the howls of frustration which
> reached us were actual sounds or only the transference
> of despairing thoughts. Indeed in this disembodied world
> it didn't seem to matter. Whatever anyone thought,
> however fleetingly or unwillingly, was instantly apparent
> to all around him, more completely than words could
> have expressed it, faster than sound waves could have
> carried it.

George Ritchie's description of this hell brings to mind the words of Jesus Christ wherein He warned that "there shall be weeping and wailing and gnashing of teeth".

Ritchie goes on to point out that one of the most frequent exchanges of thought among these spirits was one of blaming others and self-absolvement, in denial of personal responsibility for the state each individual was in. Thus these tormented souls were constantly railing against each other saying; "I told you so..." "I always knew..." "Didn't I warn you!" etc. etc.

What a picture! What an extraordinary vision of Hell. Most people are aware that solemn warnings are given in the scriptures against lascivious and unjust behaviour. But now, after reading descriptions such as the foregoing, the great logic behind the counsel to walk uprightly and remain free from vice comes to view.

The hordes of evil spirits in our midst may be classed under two categories: Millions of them are those which were cast out of Heaven, thus were never born as mortals. The others are those which have lived and died upon the earth, but were wicked in their lifetime. We know that in both categories, the evil entity will gladly enter and reside in a mortal body if a vulnerable candidate may be procured.

If possessed by an evil spirit, a person's ability to maintain long term, meaningful relationships will be severely impaired. Husbands or wives for example, if possessed by a devil, will be highly unlikely to render uncompromising fidelity to their soul mate, but rather be swayed by lusts and evil impulses. Unwholesome thoughts will spring into action resulting in sexual affairs. Surely this will not be helpful to the building of a marriage. Satan is then gratified at seeing the dissolution of what originally was supposed to have been a covenant and promise of integrity between two people.

Even on the milder end of the scale, a person possessed of evil will be crafty, contentious and self-centred. Like the man who lies to his wife about his activities and exercises cruel dominion over her, withholding access to financial and material resources to keep her in the dark and strip her of all freedom. Now of course we do not imply here that when things of this nature are occurring it is always because the perpetrator is possessed of the devil. Indeed, men and women are inwardly capable of such behaviour and do author such deeds without any help from the Devil. However, when Satan does get a foothold, such things are sure to follow.

It must be emphasised though, that we, on an individual basis, cannot assign the responsibility for our evil deeds to the Devil. While it is true that some evil doers and psychotics are compelled thus because they are host for an unseen number of evil spirits, this is by no means the rule. In other words, as stated already, plenty of the evil works that men do in this world would still be committed even if there was no Devil to incite the human race towards such actions. Either way, we are individually responsible for our actions.

Engaging upon a line of discussion such as this does raise certain questions with regard to the balance of the justice of God. Perplexities and unanswerable questions remain. We simply must always bear in mind that we do not know everything. All too often we assume too much with regards to God's purposes. Whether we recognise it or not, all things are well in hand, in the grasp of the omniscient, benevolent Master of our universe — God.

Stout scriptural warnings and indications have been given however, of how the scales of eternal justice will respond to perpetrators of serious acts such as the abuse of children and crimes against nature. In reference to the judgement of these evil doers we find sentences like: "it would be better for him if he had never been born," and "they shall be cast into outer darkness. There shall be weeping and wailing and gnashing of teeth."

Lucifer is a deceiver. He would like us to think he is a congenial gentleman who can offer alternative routes to happiness, but this will not be true in the final outcome. His entire design is to grind and sift us as wheat while gratifying himself by standing upon the heads of his subjects.

The depravity of this Being and his angels should not be underestimated. His true face may be seen in the products of his influence all around us. Films depicting murder, rape, witchcraft, hauntings, adultery, mutilations, intense hatred, etc. are reflections of his influence.

On the dark side of spiritual phenomena there are many forms of experience which demonstrate the existence of unseen evil spirits in our world. It is surprising that many people actually open the door to this enemy, and intentionally invite him in.

Take for example the effects of the ouija board. This instrument somehow provides a format by which evil, idle, and miserable spirits which normally are powerless and unseen, are then able to manifest themselves in various ways.

One woman I know whose persistent dabbling in ouija board activities resulted in the appearance of a man, or spirit rather, which she described as a greyish shadowy figure. On this occasion, after Sue's friends who had participated with her in the game of questioning the ouija board had all gone home, as she went into her bedroom, she was astonished to find this spirit sitting on her bed.

Astonished is not exactly the best choice of words, for Sue was seriously frightened. A terrible atmosphere hovered about the room and this personage, though he never spoke audibly, was looking straight at her. She demanded that he depart, to which he gave only a defiant grin. To her great despair Sue found that she could not make this entity leave. So she left. Understandably, she could not bear being alone in the house with this spirit as her only companion.

We naturally would label him as an "uninvited" guest. However, this is precisely the point. The intruder was in fact *invited* in as a result of her clandestine dabbling.

In any case, Sue ran out of the house and went in her car to seek help from a friend, who came back home with her. Just as might be expected, there was no sign of this demon, making Sue look like a fool.

In the ensuing weeks, this spirit continued to torment the lady; not by appearing visibly, which only happened the first night, but simply by making his presence felt. Somehow the invitations which had been made gave him power to intrude.

Evil apparitions do not always necessarily occur by direct invitation. While many in today's world hold the firm opinion that there are "no such things as ghosts," we have on the other hand a considerable weight of evidence that they do exist.

Obviously, this evidence consists not of tangible effects such as photographs etc., but in the fact that virtually all around the world, phenomena of this sort has been universally reported throughout the ages.

An example from among my own past acquaintances involves a man whom I shall appropriately describe as a very bitter and hard-hearted old man. I knew him while living in Nottingham in 1986.

This man was not religious in the slightest degree, nevertheless it was common knowledge among his family members that on one occasion, when he and a friend were out stealing farm produce in the night, suddenly, he saw a doorway open in the ground. A group of spirits ascended out of this portal and one of them made direct eye contact with the man.

Though he rarely spoke openly of his experience, there were occasions when he affirmed the reality of it, admitting that it was quite frightening.

While I have reason to rest assured of the veracity of the foregoing situation, such tales which get passed around are often simply not true. It seems that one of man's greatest pastimes is the fabrication of ghost stories. Nevertheless, in spite of the false claims, there really are countless authentic incidents in which these spirits have manifested themselves.

Perhaps an apparition of this type is referred to in the book of Job, Chapter 4, in which we find the words:

> Fear came upon me, and trembling, which made all my bones to shake. Then a spirit passed before my face; the hair of my flesh stood up:
>
> It stood still, but I could not discern the form thereof: an image was before mine eyes...

An experience comparable to this happened to my friend Jim. He was walking from the front door of his house, to get into his car. Suddenly, a dark spirit whose visage was not clear, appeared before him.

Jim had recently made changes in his life, in a determination to live more in keeping with righteous principles. When we spoke about this strange manifestation, He was sure that it was some kind of "lashing out" from an evil force which was opposed to the personal reforms he had made.

The existence of evil discarnate beings in our midst is also evidenced by a phenomenon which is sometimes referred to as "the old hag."

During the night, while sleeping, many people have had the experience of feeling a kind of smothering influence bearing down upon them, which in fact forces them to awaken. Aside from the cases where certain physiological causes are to blame, this sensation can indeed be attributed to an evil spirit, or spirits, which have somehow mustered the power for this moment to make their presence thus felt.

Upon awakening with a jolt, the person will usually feel a sensation of fear based on the impression that an evil predator has placed its focus upon him. Usually, the oppression will dissipate at this point, however in some instances, upon awakening, the person will actually see an entity perched upon his chest, or directly in front of his face.

If one has never had this experience, it remains difficult to grasp its reality from mere second hand information. Many however, will know exactly what I am talking about from personal experience.

As for myself, one night while sleeping, the gist of my dreams began to envelope me in an ominous evil presence. Awakening with a jolt, I saw for an instant this horrible personage sitting or crouching upon my chest. I now know why this entity has been tagged "the old hag," for in appearance, it was comparable to the stereotype image of an old, ugly, stubby witch, complete with straggly hair and wart on the nose.

The entity I saw, though having a resemblance to a horrid old woman, was like some kind of gargoyle. It seemed to have a flabby face, bulging eyes, and wiry, teased, dry hair which stood on end. To give a most tangible example, which very closely depicts the appearance of this enemy of life, I would refer to the record album from Ozzy Osborne, Diary of a Madman. Check out his photo on the back of that album and there you'll see what the demon I refer to looked like.

This is not meant as a smear to John Osborne (for such is his real name), as we may simply attribute his appearance on the said album to theatrics.

Evil attacks upon people while sleeping are not uncommon. I shall relate a bizarre experience of one particular individual whom I know very well — a member of my family.

Before doing so, it is essential that the character of the person referred to is known. In terms of having one's feet firmly on the ground and being of a sound mind, we would not find a more perfect representative. We are talking about a very pragmatic individual, who also is not inclined to mystical or spiritual experiences.

Having known this person for many years, I know that what she says in reference to her own personal experience may be relied upon as fact:

> I was sleeping, but then I was, like, up. It seemed I was still laying on my back, but out of my body.
>
> At this same instant, something, some dark force, enveloped me from behind. It wrapped around me in a very forceful grip. It was like, if a large strong person was to grab you from behind, putting his arms around your chest in a tight grip, so firmly that your arms are pinned down. This is how it felt to me. It seemed that while my head from the neck up was free, this grip was around my body, and my arms and legs could not move. However, it did not feel like a person, with arms as such, was holding me. Just an awesome intangible force, but it does seem to have seized me from behind.
>
> In the grip of this entity, I then seemed to be moving at an unbelievably fast speed, through some void. All was blackness, or, not blackness but nothingness. I was being pushed forward, travelling, like I said, at what seemed to be a very high speed.
>
> This was not a normal experience, and in fact I was frightened. It was scary, very scary. In my mind I called out to Heavenly Father, saying 'help me'. At that instant, I was freed from the force which held me bound and instantly, but somehow with a kind of thump was back in my body, in bed again. Awake, in a momentary state of paralysis and arrested breath. From this point I began to recover from the bitter ordeal.

Evaluating an experience like this can easily give rise to more questions than answers. Most medical experts, I suppose, would categorically attribute such sensations to sleep-paralysis. While it is true that sleep-paralysis does occur, causing strange sensations, this should not be assumed to be the source of all experiences such as the above. Our scientific approach to things is all too often, totally void of any consideration of the spirit. Consider the existence of gamma rays; a very short wave-length emitted by radioactive substances. We cannot see these rays naturally, yet they are real and carry a notable influence. Or take the stars for example: During the daylight, we cannot see them, but they are there. Of course these are very elementary observations, yet so it is with things of the spirit. Though we cannot see these things at present, they are nevertheless every bit as real as the material world.

With regard to the experience described above, the person is absolutely sure that it was not merely a dream. She *knows* that some dark spiritual entity took hold of her and at the instant she called out to Heavenly Father for help, the dark force was overruled and released her. It is not easy to know exactly what to make of this, but if I was to put a personal interpretation on it, taking the account fully at face value, it seems to me that on the night in question, while sleeping, this lady's spirit somehow became detached from her body, at which point an evil force seized the opportunity to more or less abduct her. It seems as though she was being rushed away. Ultimately, I suppose there is no way to really know what happened. Perhaps an extensive comparative study of experiences like this would reveal some answers.

To illustrate further the reality of this type of evil interference, I am inclined to relate other incidents that I know of first hand. Yet at the same time I am reticent to detail these things because they are so negative. I know of children who have come out of their room screaming in the night, not because of a nightmare, but because of an entity which has made an appearance, with the intent of course, to terrorise the child. Not only at night, but during the daytime as well do these apparitions alarm and terrify children.

Take Sam for example. On numerous occassions during the years in which he was between six and eight years old, he would come barreling down the stairs of his family's three story home shouting "Mum! mum! he's there again!" "Who's there Sam?" his mother would reply calmly. "The grey man!" There

were times when he insisted that his mother come up stairs and
see for herself. But of course, on arrival there was nothing
there. All Sam could do each time was insist that "He was
there."

Who can explain why a bad spirit can appear sometimes, to
some individuals, yet cannot or does not appear at other times?
Many unanswered questions remain when it comes to intangible
matters such as this. As pointed out already, pages upon pages
of similar examples could be given. However, our purpose in
this book is not to dwell on mysteries of the paranormal. The
intent here is to merely acknowledge the fact of the existence
of such things. Spiritual phenomena of this type as far as I can
see, carries with it a potent influence of misery, despair, gloom,
doom and fear. There are other far more meaningful courses of
thought to pursue.

It is beneficial to understand that we need not fear evil, by
virtue of the fact that the power of righteousness is far superior
to that of evil. We shall formulate an illustration of this with
the following scenario involving light and darkness:

Let us imagine a room with no source of light whatsoever.
At one side of the room is a closed door, on the other side of
which is another room with an ordinary 60 watt bulb burning in
a lamp in the middle of the room.

You are standing in the room which is pitch dark. So dark
that you cannot see your own hand held directly in front of
your face. As you now open the door, the light from within the
adjacent room floods into the dark space. While the room may
still be somewhat dark for lack of a direct light source within
its four walls, the darkness is nevertheless mitigated throughout.

Let us consider the reverse. Standing in the illuminated
room, you now open the door leading to the area containing
pitch darkness. Does any amount of the darkness flood into the
lighted room? No. Is the light mitigated in any degree by the
darkness? No. On the contrary, once again the light floods into
the dark space.

There is an undeniable relationship between evil and
darkness, and on the other hand, righteousness and light. The
preceding example demonstrates the dominance of light over

darkness. In like manner, the power of righteousness is far superior to the power of evil.

Looking at the world today, the Devil's work appears blatantly in every direction. Corruption among judicial leaders gnaws away at the economic balance of nations (which of course is nothing new). Murders, abuse, burglary, hatred, violence, whoredoms and even Satanic worship are among a host of wicked practices which plague our existence here, and have done so since the beginning of time, reflecting the fact that Satan and his host has been here since the beginning.

Consider though, this principle: Which of the following two assailants would be more dangerous? A man running towards you with a knife in hand and a banner over his head which reads, "I'm going to kill you," or a man who has made himself out to be your friend over time, and now walks happily beside you with a dagger hidden under his shirt? Obviously, the cunning one who has thrown up a deceptive façade is your more lethal enemy. Such is the tactic of Satan.

The "war in heaven" referred to by the title of this chapter is not simply the conflict led by Lucifer before the world began. The "war" rages on this very day and we are right in the middle of it.

For the most part in our lives, Satan keeps a fairly low profile and as per the example given above, endeavours to very carefully and cunningly drag us down. However, I am sure we have all seen times when his efforts to destroy our progress towards righteousness have been frighteningly obvious:

Recently a situation came to my attention which I feel demonstrates just how widespread and severe this war is and just how evil the adversary is:

You may have heard about Dixie Yeterian a lady with extraordinary psychic abilities which enable her to assist the police with solving serious crimes. She was so effective at perceiving the actions of criminals, to the extent of being able to envision exact addresses where abductees were being held and the locations where murder victims lay buried, that the criminal underworld put a price on her head. Thus she was forced to move away from her home in California to Anchorage, Alaska which she thought would be far enough and safe enough. Once there, law enforcement agencies—having heard of her fame—began to seek assistance. For her own safety however, she had no choice but to adopt a policy of not, absolutely not, getting involved with helping the police. She had already seen how doing so would bring the wrath of the entire criminal element down upon her. One area of law enforcement for which Dixie elected to make an exception, was the category of missing children. Using her gift, she proceeded to help the police locate these victims and apprehend their abusers.

The secret society of paedophiles now wanted Dixie dead. A murderer was hired. He showed up at her house, ordered her down on the floor and with a silenced hand-gun, shot her three times in the head. He then stabbed and beat her. Realising she was still alive, he cut her throat and then took photos of her body to collect his payment.

Miraculously, Dixie survived. In seemingly supernatural proportions, the hit man could not kill her try as he may.

The horrible reality which becomes apparent through all of this, is that in Anchorage just like so many other cities around the world, organised support promoting the evil abuse of children is so well established, that a large sum of money could be allocated for the elimination of Dixie. The evil of these child abusers runs deep enough that in addition to devouring the innocence of children, they would murder as well. Thus we see the face of Satan.

In the end, when this is over and Satan is bound, many will pass by and be surprised to see just how feeble he really is. At present, he appears to have so much power. Millions of people experience fear at times when his dark angels haunt and make their presence felt. Indeed he has the power, and intention, to lead you and I to eternal damnation. Yet it shall be as the prophet Isaiah has foretold:

> That thou shalt take up this proverb against the king of Babylon (Lucifer), and say, How hath the oppressor ceased! the golden city (the cities adorned with the wealth, riches, and material finery of society and of the world) ceased! The Lord hast broken the staff of the wicked, and the sceptre of the rulers.
>
> ...The whole earth is at rest, and is quiet: they (the inhabitants) break forth into singing. ...All they (the wicked who are brought down) shall speak and say unto thee (Lucifer), Art thou also become weak as we? art thou become like unto us? Thy pomp is brought down to the grave, How art thou fallen from heaven, O Lucifer, son of the morning! how art thou cut down to the ground, (thou) who didst weaken the nations!
>
> For thou hast said in thine heart, I will ascend into heaven, I will exalt my throne above the stars of God: I will sit also upon the mount of the congregation... I will ascend above the heights of the clouds; I will be like the most High.
>
> Yet thou shalt be brought down to hell, to the sides of the pit. They that see thee shall narrowly look upon thee, and consider thee, saying, Is this the man that made the earth to tremble, that did shake the kingdoms;

Isaiah 14:4-16

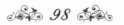

Divine Intervention

One consistent detail occurs in many near-death experiences. The person is given to understand that it is not yet time for his or her mortal period to end. Indeed, as we reflect upon the course of our own lives and upon the news we hear of others, many potential instances come to view in which our lives have been miraculously spared and our mortal period extended.

There are times when a marvelous realisation seems to open to my mind. Times when I feel in a more tangible way than ever, that our eternal Heavenly Father is near and hears the prayers of our hearts. Though we may be called to pass through the most agonizing trials—even unto suffering and death, a divine unseen power is woven into the tapestry of our existence here, guiding and aiding the course of our lives while at the same time, not interfering with our free agency or disannulling the conditions of the test.

Countless small incidents can be brought to mind where intriguing "coincidences" play a key role in situations having a significant outcome. Take for example my friend Geoff, who one evening felt a sudden compulsion to visit an elderly uncle. Geoff went to him. They had a pleasant visit during which the subject of family history, or genealogy came up. Geoff wrote down many details and some names, regarding marriages, births and deaths of people in his father's line. Some of these details were not contained among public records. The next day before noon, Geoff received a phone call informing him that his uncle had passed away in the night.

My mother has told me of the time when, during one cold winter in Ouray, Colorado, where we lived when I was a child, she was trying to get the pilot light in the furnace of our Hotel to ignite. She had been through this several times before as the old central heating furnace was temperamental. When the pilot light would go out, the residents in the building she owned would freeze, so Mom had no choice but to get down there and hold matches against the pilot needle and keep trying until it finally stayed lit. On one occasion however, she was in the middle of dealing with this problem when suddenly a strong feeling came over her that she had to drop everything and go check on her two-month-old baby, my younger brother, Brendan. The feeling was so profound that she did so, arriving just in time to save him from suffocating. Somehow he had rolled onto his face and was trapped between some cushions. When she turned Brendan over, his face was blue and he was not breathing. Luckily, she got his respiration going and he is alive and kicking today.

Another example involves a lady I know who was sewing in the kitchen with her three-month-old baby safely situated nearby in a baby-relax chair on the counter-top. For absolutely no apparent reason, this mother interrupted her work, stood up and moved the infant to the adjacent room. No sooner had she done so, than the entire kitchen ceiling came crashing down. The hot water tank above the ceiling had ruptured and saturated all the plaster and wood with water. Massive amounts of rubble came down where the baby had been only a minute before. Hillary is sure that if Liz (the baby) had still been there, the incident could well have been fatal.

Situations like these I suppose might not necessarily come under the classification of "divine intervention" as they could be attributed to moments of extra-sensory perception and spiritual gifts which sometimes are unleashed within us. In any case, they allude to divine purposes which extend beyond our knowledge of the day.

❖   ❖   ❖

Divine intervention, as such, may be more precisely defined in examples like the following:

In 1981 I was serving in the England Coventry Mission. The President of that operation had the task of presiding over some 250 missionaries spread out across the Midlands. He often had to drive long distances due to unexpected administrative necessities. On one particular occasion the fatigue which had been mounting up for some time took its toll. Late at night, as he was driving, pushing to complete the distance from Lincolnshire back to Coventry where he had appointments in the morning, he was overtaken by sleep.

The next thing he knew, he was waking up, still driving, but raising his head from an accidental slumber. At this time he distinctly and unmistakably felt a pair of hands, or something to that effect, lift off from his own hands which were gripping the steering wheel. For the reader, I suppose to some extent this will be just another fabulous story with no sure veracity. But from my perspective it is real because I know the man, and know that he is above fabricating such a story. In this case, I am sure that divine assistance saved him from a tragic outcome, which could easily have brought fatality to himself and others.

When I was thirteen years old, an incident of a miraculous nature happened when I was with a group of Boy Scouts, on a camping trip in the mountains of Colorado. We had been learning the skills of "rappelling," called "absailing" in England. This is a technique of descending the sheer face of a cliff or mountain by virtually sliding down a rope, while pushing in leaps, away from the rock face. The apparatus used involves a strong woven belt or strap which is looped around the thighs and hips and linked at the front by metal rings called karabiners. Our instructors referred to this particular harness as a "diaper." The rope is threaded through the karabiners and the person may then take up the necessary position to commence his descent.

To achieve the desired effect, the person absailing must stand right on the very edge of the cliff and lean back, holding the ropes, until he is fully perpendicular to the vertical rock face.

My turn came. With some help from a few others in the group, my apparatus was put in place. I stood on the edge, leaned back... back... back... until I was horizontal—facing the sky. To my back, was the ground approximately 200 feet below.

As I shifted the ropes to begin moving down, my waist harness and karabiner assembly suddenly came undone. Somehow an error had occurred in the way it was linked together. Considering the position I was in, literally perpendicular to the rock face with my feet against the vertical side of the cliff, I should have plummeted to the ground far below. However, I did not. I was miraculously lifted up and set upon my feet. It happened in an instant, a split second, so quickly that I and the others could not fully register what had just taken place.

To this day, I can remember the way my heart seemed to jump, and freeze, when I saw the karabiner and harness assembly come apart. A couple of my instructors and fellow scouts who were standing up top also saw it. However, the next instant, as I said, I was standing on my feet with them, with a serious gasp of relief, our shared reaction was basically; "What?!" But nothing more than that. For even though a miracle must have just occurred it was all so fast that we could only suppose I had somehow managed to throw myself upward. Somehow.

I did not feel anything lifting me, nevertheless, to this day, I cannot fathom how the law of gravity was nullified and I rose from point A to point B. Moreover, even though the experience happened to me, it is nevertheless hard to grasp... hard to believe.

Was my life spared by some unseen spiritual force? Was it simply not meant to be, that at the age of 13, I should fall to my death in a rock climbing accident? The answer has to be yes. For I know that something miraculous transpired in that moment.

Numerous situations can be cited wherein individuals have walked away from serious accidents unscathed, while in similar or identical circumstances, another individual is killed or maimed.

One example of this may be seen in an aviation disaster which occurred on January 8th, 1989, when a Boeing 737 crashed onto the M1 near Kegworth, Leicestershire, England. Out of the 125 persons on board, 32 were killed.

I remember an interesting statement made by one of the survivors who said: "I know that God saved my life. As the plane crashed, a hole opened up right beside me which made it possible for me to escape while those around me were killed."

❖   ❖   ❖

In another example, it was tuesday afternoon, June, 1996. Richard was driving home from college with a friend in the passenger seat. At about 4:30 as they were traveling on the A259 (Pevensey Marsh Road) heading from Eastbourne to Bexhill, East Sussex, Richard's vehicle was hit head-on by an on-coming car which was doing over 70mph. Richard, in his '84' Austin Maestro was doing 50mph.

The on-coming vehicle was apparently trying to overtake a slower driver which led to him speeding in the centre lane where Richard was also traveling. With a horrendous crash the two met. Immediately following this, another car barreled into the rear of Richard's auto and then yet a third car, with even greater force, slammed into the side.

With his car totally mangled, Richard climbed out through the side window, walking away with only a couple scratches. His passenger also walked away uninjured.

How? Two cars hitting head-on at 50 and 70 mph is not a trivial bump. Examining the wreckage, I saw that the passenger seat was literally squashed to less than half of its original width. Also in the place where Richard was sitting, the chassis of the car had been drastically smashed inward. The space where Richard's right leg and feet would have been was no longer there due to implosion of the car chassis and body. The front wheel assembly on the driver's side was obliterated and large pieces of steel comprising that assembly were shattered. The drive shaft was snapped and forced straight up through part of the engine and then with obvious mighty force shot through the steel car bonnet. The engine block was broken in many places. The entire car itself, dramatically folded.

It seems remarkable therefore, that the relatively fragile bodies of the two human occupants went uninjured while steel bars and other strong items around them were mangled and shattered.

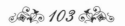

Why, and how, did these two young men survive a crash like this, totally unharmed, when thousands of people each year are maimed and killed in car accidents which in many cases are not nearly so powerful? Coincidence, luck, or divine intervention? I guess there is no way to really know.

❖   ❖   ❖

A sublime illustration of how divine intervention can shape the course of our lives, may be drawn from an incident in which my friend Simon's life was spared when he was about twelve years old.

Simon was out one day tagging along with an older friend, Elder Procter, who was about nineteen. Passing through the town centre in the busy shopping area, arriving at a pedestrian crossing, Simon and his friend stopped along with the crowd of shoppers awaiting a break in the traffic. Suddenly, Elder Procter darted across the street. A gap had appeared in the traffic, in which he knew that a quick sprint would get him across safely. Apparently, it did not occur to Procter that his young companion would blindly follow. Simon hastily stepped off the curb, heading for the other side.

Before he could take another step, an inexplicable power turned Simon back with sudden force. The boy had stepped off the curb intending to cross, but now he was right back where he started. At this same instant, a massive green bus zoomed by which would have flattened him.

This incident happened over twenty years ago, yet to this day, Simon distinctly remembers the miraculous, but seemingly unfelt force, that caused him to get out of the buses' path which he had ignorantly stepped into.

At present, this man and his wife have three children and Simon is engaged in various meaningful occupations of service to the community in which he lives. Moreover, through the years he has fulfilled other notable works.

The point to be made here, is that at the age of twelve, Simon's work in this life was not finished.

❖   ❖   ❖

Mrs. Shirley Harrison was saved during a boating trip with her family on the Colorado River when she, through an unfortunate turn of events, ended up floundering in the swift and deep currents of the river. Shirley happens to be one those people who simply cannot swim. In spite of this, she had dived into the water to save her teenage daughter and friend, who appeared to be in trouble. Paradoxically though, at the same time Shirley dived in to help, the two girls managed to scramble safely onto the opposite bank. Gerald, Shirley's husband, was some distance away untangling a boat line from some branches. The two girls ran to get his attention.

The situation became critical as the rough water swept Shirley repeatedly under. She swallowed what seemed like buckets of sandy water and was on the verge of drowning with no-one near enough to help her. She recalls thinking that it was the end and death was at hand. Suddenly, two young men were at her side in the water helping her. By this time, Gerald had become aware of her plight and came racing over in the boat to the rescue. The two young men buoyed her up while, with Gerald's help, she clambered on board. Gerald headed straight for the shore where Shirley could be given proper attention. When he turned to thank the two young heroes however, they were nowhere in sight.

Neither Gerald nor Shirley had seen the two men approach the river and jump in to save her, or come out of the water anywhere in the vicinity of the incident. The banks along this particular stretch were barren and clear of obstructions for a considerable distance. In fine, the young men were never seen by anyone of Shirley's group other than at the moment they were in the water helping her.

Where did the two heroes come from and where did they vanish to afterward?

From a purely academic perspective we must simply assume that the two young men helped this lady and then slipped away undetected. Nevertheless, to Shirley, Gerald, and the others present it was an extraordinary event. "You had to have been there to really see what I mean." Gerald explained. "It's just odd how two guys can suddenly appear out of nowhere like that in the water, and then be gone when you turn around to thank 'em. ...It's hard to figure how no-one saw these guys anywhere on the shore at any time before or after Shirley's accident."

What is sure, is that through the sheer luck of those two men showing up when they did, Shirley's life was spared. That in itself is the point.

❖ ❖ ❖

Hello L.A.

A scrape with death in which my escape seems to have come by divine providence occurred in November 1985, in the heart of Los Angeles. I refer to the night when I was murdered — almost.

As mentioned earlier, I used to live in Denver, Colorado. In 1985 the employment situation in that city took a real dive, so after a phone call to my brother who was at the time a student at Pasadena College near Los Angeles, I decided to move to California thinking it would be easier to find worthwhile employment there. Two weeks later, after making all the necessary preparations, I boarded a coach bound for Los Angeles. At about 9:45 p.m. the next evening the coach arrived at its destination, and there I was at the main bus depot in the middle of the big city of L.A.

I had never been to L.A. before. It was all new to me. Hefting all my belongings with me, I wandered around the station for a short time trying to figure out how I would complete the last leg of my journey to Pasadena, about 40 minutes away.

At the information counter, I was informed that there were no more coaches to Pasadena until 6:00 the next morning. This meant I would have to hang around the station all night waiting for the next coach. The waiting facilities at this station were not at all comfortable and I was not enamoured with the idea of being there all night.

The place was full of people, some of whom gave me the creeps. I was approached a number of times by pushers of mysterious substances. One man produced a fistful of long sticks of dried leaves and said to me, "Twenty-five dollars a piece." I suppose it was Cannabis. He seemed offended at my response which basically was, "I'll pretend I didn't see that." I moved on.

Other individuals lingering about the premises seemed acutely curious about my baggage. Especially my satchel wondering what it might contain and would it be profitable to remove the item from me.

Upon further inquiry, I learned that outside of the station, about 5 blocks down the Boulevard, I could catch a local bus which would take me to Pasadena where my brother was waiting to accommodate me.

I headed out, loaded down with a large, fully packed army duffel bag strapped on my back, plus two guitars, one slung over my shoulder and the other carried in its case by the handle. And last but not least, a satchel full of cassette tapes, a walkman, and my books of scriptures. As I made my way down the street, it became increasingly apparent that I was in a very bad place for this time of night. Anyone who is familiar with downtown Los Angeles can wholeheartedly affirm that the vicinity of the Continental Trailways station is no place to go walking about after dark. However, I was not aware of this fact at the time.

As I proceeded down the Boulevard, all around were the towering buildings of the city. The city I had seen many times on television, but never in real life. The street however, seemed dirty and run-down, unlike what I had always envisioned the "glamorous" city of L.A. to be like. There were pockets of people, idly standing around in dark corners everywhere. I noticed a woman, black hair, tall black boots, fishnet stockings and a red mini-skirt, walking towards me. As we passed on the sidewalk, something about this personage seemed terribly distorted. I suddenly realised it was a man — but now was transvested into something which was neither man nor woman.

About this time, I arrived at the bus stop which indicated Pasadena on its schedule. I was standing there, waiting, when a group of men who did not look very friendly came shuffling over and surrounded me. The tallest of them (and he was a fair bit taller than I), held out his hand, opened it, and said to me; "Fifteen dollars!" In his hand were two little white beads. I figured it was some kind of drug. I tried not to notice and mumbled; "I'm waiting for a bus." His reply to this was; "Ten Dollars for the small one!" I said no thanks. Immediately he started leaning threateningly close to me. He was angry and demanded "Where's my money!" My *unspoken* reply was 'excuse me but I haven't made a purchase.' I tried to ignore the situation. The fiery hatred and anger in his eyes was counteracted by a cold glazed look. The next thing I knew, something like a cord or heavy wire went around my neck which at the same instant, tightened to the maximum. I was immobilized by the person from behind who had put the stranglehold on me. I was then pulled backward off my feet and dragged into the darkness of a dank alley.

There was no circulation to my head. I could not breath. The cord around my neck was so extremely tight, that I could not even whisper, or make any sound whatsoever.

Everything went all fluffy in my mind. I didn't even have enough consciousness left to be afraid. I was at that point where you know you are finished and that's it. Death was imminent.

In the depths of my heart, I directed my thoughts to God and basically said very hastily: 'Oh God if you don't do something, I'll be seeing you real soon!' At this very instant the cord was released. I was on the ground but somehow managed to get up on my feet — still loaded down with all my possessions. The life saving blood was rushing again through my head. I could breath again though at this moment everything was still quite muffled. I faintly heard one of the assailants say demandingly; "Okay; take out your wallet."

At this, I suddenly had a brilliant stroke of inspiration: Run! I bolted. Even though the men (about eight in all), had encircled me, I barreled through them like a bowling ball knocking down pins. Moving at top speed, as I exited the alley and was running down the street, I detected that my ill-mannered friends were in hot pursuit. It now seemed that the best thing to do, was to run into the middle of the street and make like a car. I remember thinking that I would rather get hit by a car than fall into those turkeys' hands again. 'At least if I get hit by a car, an ambulance will be called,' I hoped.

Well, they lost interest when they saw me out there dodging Chevys.

Needless to say, I thought it best not to go back to the bus stop. Plus, I had probably missed it by now anyway. I decided to go back to the Continental Trailways Bus Station, but there was a new problem. I was lost. I asked a passer-by for directions, which he gave and in five minutes I was back at the station, forced to be satisfied waiting for the morning coach to Pasadena.

One pertinent question which may be raised hinges on the fact that precisely at the moment when I called out in my heart to God, the cord was released from my neck. I was at the brink of death. Was my life saved by the power of God? On one hand we can easily say there is no proof of this — for indeed, perhaps those men would have released the cord anyway. The indisputable fact though, is that when in my heart I called for God's help at the crucial moment, the release was instantaneous.

❖   ❖   ❖

A boy and his Turtle

I shall here relate an extraordinary, but perhaps unimportant miracle which took place when I was about ten years old.

We lived in a large house in Denver Colorado at the time. At this age, I had a fascination with reptiles and amphibians and always managed to ferret out local ponds and fields, where I could collect tadpoles, garter snakes, lizards and so on. I would bring these things home in mayonnaise jars with perforated lids — the usual scenario. And of course, as per the usual scenario, these creatures would either die in my well meaning care, or get lucky and escape.

It was an age when turtles, frogs and even Cecropia moth cocoons held a beauty which seems to have vanished as I gradually matured in years. I faintly recall a time when going to school with a toad in my pocket was perfectly satisfying.

One glorious day, my uncle brought me a tortoise which he had almost flattened with his car, as the animal was obliviously crossing a motorway. It was an Ornate Box Turtle (which is

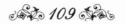

actually a *tortoise*) with a shell breadth of about 5 inches. I was elated.

An appropriate name for him came to mind within a day, when the turtle reached out, with beak wide open, and clamped down on the side of my hand. I screamed of course and shook the monster loose. This event motivated me to call him "Hot Jaws".

He was ornery! Whenever I picked him up, he would stretch his neck around with an open beak in an attempt to fasten once more on any part of me that he might catch. I was careful though and knew how to avoid his bite, having learned by painful experience!

I made allowances for his ill-mannered behaviour and loved him in spite of his faults. I even forgave him for the time when he clamped down on my best friend's finger.

Later that year, in the midst of a wonderful summer, I often took advantage of the warm weather by sleeping outside. Our house on Decature Street had a spacious back yard, about half an acre in size. Camping out overnight was great fun. My little brother, Brendan, would often camp with me. For him however, the adventure often lost its savour at about 1:00 am. When I would wake up at dawn with my face wet from the morning dew and the blankets damp (for we did not use a tent, but slept under the beautiful roof of stars), Brendan's bedding was usually empty, and he, could be found secure and warm in his own bed in the house.

I recall one evening when I decided to sleep outside. After coercing my mother for permission again, I commenced hauling the usual load of blankets outside to get set up. On this particular occasion, neither my brother nor any of my sisters wanted to join in on the fun, so I had the brilliant idea of having Hot Jaws join in the adventure. I put my friend in a bucket with some leaves and dry grass and we bedded down for the night in the back yard.

At dawn came the usual song of the Red-Wing Blackbird which led the way as all the other feathered creatures gradually joined in. I eventually looked in the bucket beside me and was shocked to find that Hot Jaws was not there!

It was hard for me to believe it. I looked in the bucket over and over again, shuffling my hand through the leaves and grass, but he was gone. I began to search around the immediate area through the bushes and grass. Along the fenced perimeter I scrutinized the neighbours' gardens trying to spot him. I completed a thorough search of the entire area but finished in disappointment and sat down on a brick encasement of a flower bed. After mustering new energy, having convinced myself that another try would be successful, I searched again endeavouring to cover every inch of a rather large yard, with no luck.

The next event may seem a bit peculiar to some people, nevertheless, at this point; I knelt upon the ground near the back of the house, and prayed to Heavenly Father, asking him to help me find my turtle. Arising, I searched the yard intensely once again, only to come back empty handed.

Without hesitation I knelt down again at the same spot and said to Heavenly Father: "I didn't find him yet, so I'm going to try again now." I searched again, with no luck. I recall going a third time to Heavenly Father with undaunted patience and faith. I simply asked him again, "please help me find Hot Jaws." What happened next was a miracle.

I stood up and walked without any particular haste. I did not feel anything guiding me or hear any voices, but walked towards the far end of the yard. Arriving in a patch of overgrown grass, with a few weeds and a layer of compost from accumulations of fallen leaves, I stopped. I bent down and probed with my fingertips through the grass and compost until I could feel the soil. Probing further, about an inch below the surface of the ground, I recall so vividly, feeling at the tip of my fingers, his shell. I cleared away the dirt and pulled out of the ground, my turtle.

Delighted, I looked up and thanked Heavenly Father, believing that He had helped me find my pet, but even so, I did not realise then how remarkable of a miracle had just transpired!

How is it that I stood up from my third prayer and just automatically walked straight to the spot where the tortoise was concealed below the surface of the ground?

In all my searching prior to that moment, I had not taken the approach of excavating pieces of ground, for in spite of my boyish general knowledge of turtles, I actually did not know at that age about their propensity to burrow. Hot Jaws never burrowed in the glass terrarium in which I kept him in the house (because of insufficient depth in the gravel of course).

All of my expectations were that if I did find him, he would be crawling through the grass, or sitting in deep thought under a bush, maybe covered by leaves but not buried under the dirt.

How is it that I stopped at the exact spot where, if I was to stoop down and insert my fingers in the ground he would be there? There were no visible signs of him as the tall grass, leaves, and weeds shrouded the surface of the soil.

❖   ❖   ❖

As a boy, there were many times that I went to Heavenly Father with difficulties and He responded to my petitions. The problem with trying to share these events is that they will for most observers, appear as mere insignificant coincidences. Moreover, many such experiences are too sacred and personal to reveal.

When people talk about the way a prayer has been answered by God, our natural tendency is to feel that this person is making a big deal out of nothing, looking for miracles. Nevertheless, these experiences will often be, in reality, precious intimations of our Heavenly Father's love. An example of this is seen in the following recollection:

When I was living on Decature Street, I attended Ashland Elementary school. There were a lot of kids there who seemed eager to find someone to dominate and terrorise. This one kid chose me. He was a couple years older, and for assorted reasons was somewhat frightening. Day after day he used to show up out of nowhere, threatening me with being beaten up after school. Demanding money. Criticising my shoes, my hair, trousers, etc. The worst thing however, was the way he managed to instill a terrible constant feeling of fear into me when it came to going to school. I dreaded running into him. To a ten-year-old kid, things can be very serious which to an adult of course would be trivial.

I recall kneeling down in the privacy of my Dad's study one morning before school, pouring my heart out to Heavenly

Father. I told Him that if it was His will to place trials like this upon me, I was willing to endure and try to face them, but with perhaps even more conviction, I pleaded with Him for a way out of the torment I was feeling.

Within the next day or two, my problem was resolved as follows: My mother sent me to get a carton of milk from the nearby Safeway store. While there, guess who I saw? That kid! My fear of him had been so compounded over the weeks that my reaction would have been to avoid the bully at all costs, evading him between the isles, making sure that he did not see me there at the supermarket because once outside, he would have come after me. Instead of reacting this way however, a tremendous inner strength came over me. I went directly over and informed him that I was not going to tolerate his threats any more and with a burst of energy, gave him a forceful shove from which he fell backwards into the milk cooler. With him in that position I remember saying, "if you approach me any more at school, this is what your gonna get." He never ever bothered me again, and in fact seemed to avoid me.

I could go on naming incidents where my sincere petitions to God have been followed by pertinent events, which indeed have formed solutions or answers to voiced concerns.

While it is futile to endeavour to prove categorically that God answers prayers and that a divine influence watches over our lives, the foregoing examples indicate the reality of these things. If an insignificant matter such as a boy who wants to find his turtle can be heard and answered by our kind Eternal Father, then certainly the same is true for matters of greater concern which we face in life.

Often times our situation may be compared to that of a parakeet, a budgie or other small bird in a cage which hangs in a room where there is a table nearby. The table is near enough that the other household pet, the Cat, can sit for hours in fascination by the cage, watching the bird flutter and hop about.

Now suppose the Lady of the House passes by and sees this. "No worries," she says within herself. "I have secured the cage; there is no way that Sylvester can harm Tweety." Unfortunately, Tweety doesn't know that. He lives in daily terror because of his instinctive knowledge that this cat will eat him for lunch if given the chance.

 113

It has been known to happen that a domestic cage bird has literally died of fright when in reality the bird was quite safe. Yes, to a large extent, we are like that bird: In life there are constant major threats staring us in the face. We sometimes live in fear over some imaginary threat, which in reality never will come upon us.

The big difference though, between our situation and that of the frightened bird in a cage, is the bird is actually safe, though he doesn't know it. We on the other hand may or may not be. An endless list of dangers, diseases or misfortunes could actually befall any of us at any time.

Dwelling on this fact can actually become very destructive to one's life. One man in particular that I know, was reduced from a healthy outgoing person to a quivering bundle of nerves through constantly imagining all the different bad things which might happen to him. For two years he spent most of his life in various wards of the hospital, even though the doctors could not find anything physically wrong with him.

The psychosomatic nature of his ailment was demonstrated by the way he became convinced that his body was slowly filling up with water. His feet filled up first and over the months, the water level reached his rib-cage, he thought. He was sure that when it got up to his neck he would expire. He lived in a panic over this impending doom, insisting that the doctors had to accept his self diagnosis and devise a treatment. But in reality this was all a fixation in his mind.

A lady I knew had a set of family medical encyclopedias which she used to read daily. She discovered so many ailments which can befall the human body, that she found herself becoming more and more distressed with worry and began to notice many symptoms. Laying awake at night in consternation over which ailments she might have, the cycle would compound itself when with a shock it would occur to her that 'insomnia', she had read, was also a symptom of this or that illness.

If we can master the ability to not worry about things, life will be abundantly more beautiful and peaceful, for as stated, we often endure relentless anxiety worrying about things which never happen.

A tremendous amount of inspiration may be derived from the near-death experiences which are occurring so abundantly in this age. Intrinsic in these events is the beautiful concept that truly, there is a divine power which reigns over all that transpires here.

A marvelous key to eliminating some of life's worry and stress is to instill an eternal perspective in our daily walk. To define this eternal perspective in concise terms, the facts are thus: This life is only a brief moment in the overall span of our existence. Even if we should live to be 120 years old, this would still be nothing more than a flash, a twinkling of an eye, when weighed in the balance of the endless course of eternity — which you and I have walked and will continue to walk.

We are the offspring of an eternal being, hence, eternal beings ourselves. Exercising the godly potential and qualities within us, will ensure that the divine purpose of our time here does not go unfulfilled. On this basis, divine intervention, protection, and guidance is happening all around us, all the time.

❖   ❖   ❖

Precious further insight into the purpose of our lives, and certain aspects of the realm to which the inhabitants of this earth go after death comes to us from Heber G. Haley, who in 1920 was conducted on a remarkable brief sojourn through the spirit world.

At a Genealogical Conference held in October of 1920, Heber related his experience at the request of the First Presidency of the Church of Jesus Christ of Latter-Day Saints. From the transcript of his narrative I give the following excerpts:

The Heavenly Manifestation Given To
Heber G Haley
President Of Boise Idaho Stake

It is with a very humble and grateful spirit that I attempt to relate on this occasion, by request, a personal experience that is very sacred to me. I must of necessity be brief. Furthermore, there were certain things made known to me which I don't feel at liberty to relate here. Let me say by

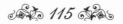

way of preface that between the hours of 12 and 7:30 in the night of January 20, 1920, while alone in the room at the home of W.F. Rawson in Carry, Idaho, this glorious manifestation was vouchsafed to me.

(...)

I passed but a short distance from my body through a film into the world of spirits. This was my first experience after going to sleep. I seemed to realize that I had passed through the change called death and I so referred to it in my conversation with the immortal beings with whom I immediately came into contact. I readily observed their displeasure at our use of the word death and the fear which we attached to it. They used there another word in referring to the transition from mortality to immortality, which word I don't recall, and I can only approach its meaning and the impression which was left upon my mind, by calling it 'the New Birth'.

My first visual impression was the nearness of the world of spirits to the world of mortality. The vastness of this heavenly sphere was bewildering to the eyes of the spirit-novice. Many enjoyed unrestricted vision, and unimpeded action, while many others were visibly restricted as to both vision and action. The vegetation and landscape were beautiful beyond description; not all green as here, but gold with varying shades of pink, orange, and lavender... as the rainbow. A sweet calmness pervaded everything. The people I met there I did not think of as spirits, but as men and women, self-thinking and self-acting individuals, going about important business in a most orderly manner. There was perfect order there and everybody had something to do and seemed to be about their business.

That the inhabitants of the spirit world are classified according to their lives of purity and their compliance with the Father's will, was subsequently made apparent. Particularly was it observed that the wicked and unrepentant are confined to a certain district by themselves, the limits of which are as definitely determined and impassable as the line marking the division of the physical from the spiritual world. A mere film, but impassable until the person himself was changed. The world of spirit was the temporary abode of all spirits pending the resurrection from the dead and the judgment. There was much activity within the different spheres, and appointed ministers of salvation were seen coming from the higher to the lower spheres in pursuit of their missionary appointments.

I had a very pronounced desire to meet certain of my kinsfolk and friends, but I was at once impressed with the fact that I had entered a tremendously great and intensive world, even greater than our earth and more abundantly inhabited. I could be in only one place at a time, could do only one thing at a time, could look only in one direction at a time, and accordingly it would require many, many years to search out and converse with all those I had known and those whom I desired to meet unless they were especially summoned to receive me. All men and women were appointed to special and regular service under a well organized plan of action, directed principally toward preaching the gospel to the unconverted, teaching those who seek knowledge and establishing family relationships and gathering genealogies for the use and benefit of mortal survivors of their respective families, that the work of baptism and the mortal ordinances may be vicariously performed for the departed in the Temples of God upon the Earth. The authorized representatives of families in the world of spirits have access to our Temple records and are kept fully advised of the work done here. The work performed in the Temple however, does not become automatically effective. The recipients must first believe, repent and accept baptism and confirmation then certain consummating ordinances are performed in the spirit world effectualizing these saving principles in the lives of those regenerated beings. And so the great work is going on — they are doing a work there which we cannot do here, and we a work here which they cannot do there for the salvation of all God's children who will be saved.

I was surprised to find there no babies in arms. I met the infant son of Orsen W. Rawlings, my first counselor. I immediately recognized him as the baby who died a few years ago, and yet he seemed to have the intelligence and, in certain respect, the appearance of an adult, and was engaged in matters pertaining to his family and its genealogy. My mind was quite contented upon the point that mothers will again receive into their arms their children who died in infancy and will be fully satisfied, but the fact remains that entrance into the world of spirits is not an inhabitation of growth but the greatest opportunity of development. Babies are adult spirits in infant bodies.

(...)

I moved forward covering an appreciable distance and consuming considerable time, viewing the wonderful sights of landscape, parks, trees, and flowers and meeting people some of whom I knew, but thousands of whom I did not recognize as acquaintances. I presently approached a small group of men, standing in a path lined with spacious stretches of flowers, grasses, and shrubbery, all of a golden hue, marking the approach of a beautiful building. The group was engaged in earnest conversation. One of their number parted from the rest and came walking down the path. I at once recognized my esteemed President Joseph F. Smith. He embraced me as a father would his son and after a few words of greeting, quickly remarked: "You have not come to stay" which remark I understood more as a declaration than an interrogation. For the first time I became fully conscious of my uncompleted mission on earth and, as much as I would have liked to remain, I at once asked President Smith if I might return...

(...)

From a certain point of vantage, I was permitted to view this earth and what was going on here. There was no limitation of my vision and I was astounded at this. I saw my wife and children at home. I saw President Heber J. Grant at the head of the great Church and Kingdom of God and felt the divine power that radiates from God giving it light and truth and guiding its destiny. I beheld this nation founded as it is upon correct principles and designed to endure, but beset by evil and sinister forces that seek to lead men to thwart the purposes of God. I saw towns and cities; the sins and wickedness of men and women. I saw vessels sailing the oceans and scanned the battle-scarred fields of France and Belgium. In a word, I beheld the whole world, as if it was but a panorama passing before my eyes. Then there came to me the unmistakable impression that the earth and scenes and persons upon it are open to the vision of the spirits only when special permission is given or when they are assigned to special service here. This is particularly true of the righteous who are busily engaged in two fields of activity at the same time. The wicked and unrepentant have still, like the rest, their free agency, and applying themselves to no useful or wholesome undertaking, seek pleasure about their old haunts and exalt in the sin and wickedness of degenerate humanity. To this extent they are still the tools of Satan. It is these idle, mischievous and deceptive spirits who appear as miserable counterfeits at spiritualist seances, table dancing and ouija board operation. The noble and great ones do not respond to the call of the mediums and to every curios group of meddlesome inquirers. They would not do it in the world of mortality, certainly they would not do it in their increased state of knowledge in the world of immortality. These wicked and unrepentant spirits are allies of Satan and his hosts, operating through willing mediums in the flesh. These three forces constitute an unholy trinity upon the earth, and are responsible for sin, wickedness, distress, and misery among men and nations.

I moved forward feasting my eyes upon the beauty of everything about me and glorying in the indescribable peace and happiness that abounded in everybody and through everything. The further I went, the more glorious things appeared. While standing at a wonderfully beautiful Temple capped with golden domes, there emerged a small group of men dressed in white robes who paused for a brief conversation. They were the first I had seen thus clad.

(...)

President Smith informed me that I had been given permission to return and complete the mission upon the earth which the Lord had appointed me to fulfill, and then with his hand upon my shoulder, uttered these memorable and significant words. 'Brother Heber, you have a great work to do. Go forward with a prayerful heart and thou shalt be blessed in your ministry. From this time on, never doubt that God lives, that Jesus Christ is the Son, the Savior of the world, that the Holy Ghost is a God of Spirit and the messenger of the Father and Son; never doubt the resurrection of the dead, the immortality of the soul; that the destiny of man is eternal progress. Never again doubt that the mission of the Latter-Day Saints is to all mankind, both the living and the dead; and that the great work in the holy Temples was sent of God to usher in the Gospel dispensation of the Fullness of Times, which is the last unto mortals upon the earth. His successors have all been called of and approved of God. President Heber J. Grant is at this time the recognized and ordained head of the Church of Jesus Christ upon the earth. Give him your confidence and support. Much you have seen and heard here you will not be permitted to repeat when you return.' Thus saying, he bade me goodby, and God bless you.

Quite a distance, through various scenes, and passing innumerable people, I traveled before I reached the sphere which I had first entered. On my way I was greeted by many friends and relatives, certain of whom sent words of greeting and counsel to their dear ones here, my mother being one of them. One other I will mention. I met Brother John Adamson, his wife, his son James and their daughter Isabelle, all of whom were killed by the hand of a foul assassin in their home at Carey, Idaho, in the evening of October 29, 1915. They seemed to define that I was on my way back to mortality and immediately said, (Brother Adamson was speaking) 'Tell the children that we are very happy and very busy and they should not mourn our departure, nor worry their minds over the manner by which we were taken. There is a purpose in it, and we have a work to do here which required our collective efforts, and which we could not do individually.' I was at once made to know that the work referred to was that of genealogy on which they were working in England and Scotland.

One of the grandest and most sacred things of heaven is the family relationship. The establishment of a complete chain without any broken links brings a fullness of joy. The ordinances of baptism, endowment, and sealings performed in the Temples of God by the living for the dead are the welding of the links. Ordinances are performed in the spirit world effectualising the individual recipient for their receiving the saving principles of the Gospel vicariously performed here.

As I was approaching the place where I entered, my attention was attracted towards a number of small groups of women, preparing what appeared to me wearing apparel. Observing my inquiring countenance one of the women remarked, 'We are preparing to receive Brother Philip Worthington very soon.' As I gasped his name in repetition I was admonished, 'If you knew the joy and the glorious mission that awaits him here you would not ask to have him longer detained upon the earth.'

Philip Worthington died January 22, 1920, for which I was advised by telegram and returning to Boise, preached his funeral sermon on January 25, 1920.

(...)

To the righteous person, birth into the world of spirits (or death as we call it) is a glorious privilege and blessing. The greatest spirits in the family of the Father have not usually been permitted to tarry longer in the flesh than to perform a certain mission; then they are called to the world of spirits where the field is greater and the workers fewer.

I passed quietly out where I had entered the world of spirits and immediately my body was quickened, and I was left to ponder over and record the many wonderful things I had seen and heard.

❖ ❖ ❖

Several profound insights may be gained from the experience of Heber G. Haley. However, as he himself states, there were certain things which he did not feel at liberty to disclose on that occasion. This is perhaps due in part to the skepticism with which people would receive his statements.

In this world we hear many view points regarding the existence, or non-existence of God. Recent national surveys (September 1996) show that while a notable percentage of people claim to believe in God in some form or another, the vast majority are of the opinion that He is not a personal God, but a force, "perhaps an intelligence of some kind."

At the opposite far end of the spectrum is the category of people who are inordinately convinced that God rules every second in every moment of our lives.

The experience of my life has nurtured the conviction that neither of the above are correct. I believe that God is literally our eternal Heavenly Father. Willing and able to hear our prayers and influence the events in our lives, while also remaining aloof somewhat — allowing us to turn each blank page and do the writing thereon, as we exercise free agency in what we do with our days.

Things have happened which make me believe that He is interested in our trivial matters, if for no other reason than simply that He loves us, as a righteous parent naturally loves an infant. This love that our Heavenly Father has toward us is of course not always apparent. In fact, judging by the trials and misfortunes in the lives of some people it appears totally non-existent. A few of the reasons for this however are tentatively illustrated in the opening chapter of this book.

If the Truth Be Known

The nature of subject matter in this book brings us repeatedly to the level of a religious discussion, which can be a very touchy subject to get entangled with.

Regarding Christianity in general, the total disenchantment many people feel towards this religion is due in part to the falsehoods which canker many religious sects as well as major organisations.

The name of Christianity has been badly tarnished by hypocrites and corrupt teachings to the extent that the minute Christ's name is even mentioned, people turn off and just don't want to know.

The Bible itself, though one of the most ancient literary works in existence, is often viewed with disdain by those who have been exposed to some of the more nauseous brands of pandemonious Christian focus. Notwithstanding the presence of this extensive religious record, the plethora of different Christian denominations extant in the world appears to be in somewhat of a chaotic state and has been for quite some time. Especially in America where commercialised Christianity has become a veritable circus.

It is not my intention to be offensive to any particular group, but, there are some culprits out there. One crime which some are guilty of is teaching false doctrine. This though, is a rather subjective ground upon which to accuse a specific target, for what may appear as false doctrine to one individual, may be the sincerely treasured belief of another. We shall speak more of the contrast between truth and error in a moment.

A much more definitive ground upon which we may judge the integrity of a religious movement and its proponents, arises when it is discovered that the party in question is an outright scam.

While on one hand we should be tolerant of religious creeds which differ from our own, we at the same time are not obligated to welcome and accept movements which are perpetrated by fanatics, mad-men, and false prophets. Prime examples of which are "The Peoples Temple Church" led by the self-appointed Reverend Jim Jones, proclaiming himself to be "God's heir on earth." One of the tactics Jones used to build up his following was the staging of fake healing exhibitions. He set up his own religious creed, denouncing the Bible as merely an idol, while at the same time proclaiming his church to be a Christian denomination. In 1964 he prophesied that the world would end on the 15th of July, 1967, through a nuclear holocaust. In spite of this and other failed prophecies, the sect continued until 1978 when on the 18th of November, 913 members of the sect were persuaded to drink a leathal concoction laced with cyanide. Thus, the influence of Jim Jones over his followers culminated in a mass suicide in Guyana, South America.

Hundreds of bloated bodies were found strewn over the ground at the "Jonestown" settlement. Overlooking the morbid scene was a large sign, posted by Jones and his dupes which read "THOSE WHO FORGET THE PAST ARE DOOMED TO REPEAT IT."

Jones was at least right about one thing. Take for instance the Waco Texas incident. David Koresh, became the influencial leader of a sect in which once again, the followers were led to their deaths.

To his disciples, Koresh was the "messiah," standing-in for Christ until his second coming which Koresh said was to occur in 1993. Like so many of these evil cults, the creed which Koresh set up involved sexual practices which gave him privileges with the women of his church, including very young women.

On February 28, 1993, law enforcement agencies including the ATF and the FBI laid siege to the stronghold Koresh had established in Waco. Towards the end of the 51 day stand-off, he ordered the entire premises to be doused with kerosene. The inmates which did try to leave were shot. At Koresh's command, the kerosene was ignited and the ranch was rapidly engulfed in flames. 85 people met their death in that tragedy.

We could also cite the evil work of Ervil Le Baron which spawned the murder of innocent people, all in the name of God.

Less blatant but more numerous are the con-organisations which, posing as ministries representing Jesus, swindle people out of their "unnecessary baggage;" their money. Some of these "wolves in sheep's clothing" with the all too common motive of financial gain, have an astonishingly direct approach. I recall one evangelist in particular who regularly advertised on television, proclaiming in a strong southern accent, "Yes! Fa only ten dolla's, ya'll can ha'ave salvation!" For this fee you would receive a copy of his "works every time" prayer formula and some other tracts.

Before moving to England I lived in Denver Colorado, and then in Los Angeles. In both cities I noticed that along with round the clock sports, vintage comedy re-runs, action movies and news, many of the television stations also provided a great selection of TV Evangelists to watch. Now as far as entertainment goes, this was often more enthralling than any fictionalised production. Here, we had real-life drama, amazingly out of touch with reality. True life absurdity which could rival the comical re-runs of Gilligan's Island.

You had to be there. I suppose some readers may underestimate the absolute chicanery I refer to. But you have to have seen these clowns in action to really get the gist of what I'm saying.

America sat in amazement, or shall I say amusement when a certain nationally known television Evangelist (I'll refrain from using names) came on the screen to inform us, that God had informed him, that unless we, the viewers, could come up with something like 12 million dollars in donations for ambitious projects of his ministry, God was going to exterminate the said evangelist. He had 30 days to achieve the financial demand that had been placed upon him.

Over the ensuing weeks this person would come onto his show with a red thermometer board, showing the gradual increase of the "desperately" needed amount. Some days he would nearly produce feigned tears in supplication to his viewers, to send in the money. Luckily for him, the goal was reached just before God would have given him the chop.

There was another TV evangelism empire which was owned and hosted by a certain man and wife team. All in the happy name of Jesus they raked in copious funds until being exposed for misappropriating and embezzling millions of dollars, which according to their television campaigns were to be used for various charitable endeavours.

America was appalled at seeing the lavish homes which these people had purchased with the donations of their faithful viewers. Their frivolous use of funds was epitomised in the press exposure of a dog house equipped with central heating and air conditioning; unfortunately their dog would not go near it!

The reports of this couple's antics and the immoral activities they got up to in their personal lives became international news. Phil Collins certainly heard about it as his hit song and video "Jesus he knows me" was obviously based on this story.

I suppose we did get value for money from our hosts in one respect. Every morning, afternoon and evening, you could tune in and be greeted with glorious happy smiles, bubbly personalities and friendly faces sharing liberally, "the good news of Jesus." So this was fine as long as you didn't know about the lavish homes they were amassing through your donations. The illicit affairs, the frolicking naked in men's locker rooms, the drug abuse, the embezzlement of funds and in general, the lies.

Television evangelism is still going strong in the USA, however I have no familiarity with the current programmes, having resided in England for the past ten years. Perhaps some of those currently operating evangelists would be cross with me for writing these criticisms. Some may feel that I am giving this brand of Christianity a bad name. On the contrary, it is not I, but the culprits of whom I speak who give TV evangelism a bad name. Indeed these comments are not to be taken generally. Just because one is bad doesn't mean they all are. These specific cases of which I speak were unimpeachably exposed as frauds and hypocrites, and their iniquities were "spoken upon the housetops" in the sense that millions of people around the world received the reports through television antennae mounted upon their housetops.

Another real classic, involves an evangelist who toured the country putting on massive healing exhibitions where, as if by some great spiritual gift, he would "perceive" the name of a person in his studio audience. Calling this individual forward, he would proceed to recite the person's address or the nature of his ailment and so on. By now, the unsuspecting punter is totally impressed and amazed that this evangelist could receive such precise revelation about him. The showman is now bobbing up and down with excitement. In a high screechy voice he brays "Come on down here and feel the power of Jee-suss!" Then in an even louder voice he shrieks at the audience "Let's make the devil mad!" By now the audience is also going wild. People are seen leaping to their feet shouting "Hallelujah!" while others just as rapidly are falling to the floor, overcome by something.

The eager man from the audience arrives on stage. The healer approaches, slams the poor guy on the forehead so hard that he falls on the floor, and when he gets up, all of his problems are over. He has "Jee-suss" now and is healed of whatever it was that ailed him. The evangelist now receives another name to call out, and the process is repeated.

I was about 17 years old when these healing exhibitions were aired every Saturday and Sunday morning on channel Two. I found them entertaining, yet somewhat sickening. After every show, the evangelist would make a solo appearance and appeal to his viewers for "desperately needed" donations. "Jee-suss needs your money, not me. Show Jesus you love him. If you don't send a donation, it's Jesus your turning away, not me."

This lucrative scam was brought to its knees in humiliation when the results of a covert investigation were broadcast on national TV in the documentary, "60 Minutes." It was discovered that the Evangelist would conceal a tiny receiver in his ear, by which he could listen to information from his accomplice — his wife — who from back stage would transmit details about specific individuals. These bits of information were collected by operatives using various tactics, from people who had booked seats and from those waiting outside the doors of the stadium or auditorium prior to the big show.

The conviction leveled against this racket in the 60 Minutes exposure was solid. When the investigative reporters had sussed out the man's game, it was at first kept hush hush. Then, they simply approached and flattered the evangelist, informing him that the prestigous, nationally syndicated documentary, 60 Minutes, was interested in doing a slot on his extraordinary healing exhibitions, asking if they could film one.

Permission was readily granted. What the evangelist and his team did not know, was that the investigative team had discovered the frequency of his receiver.

The stage was now set. The 60 Minutes camera-men, equipped with a receiver tuned and ready to pick up whatever would be secretly transmitted to the ear of our entertainer, filmed the exhibition.

Thus what we saw and heard in the documentary was the evangelist on stage, preaching to his audience as normal, yet out of the blue we would hear a woman's voice, which would give a name—which thereupon the evangelist would feign to have received by revelation. Then we would hear the mystery voice give some additional detail like an address or special concern of the individual. The evangelist, smooth as silk, would then work this information into his routine. This evangelistic operation was a complete pack of lies.

It looks as though this particular scenario was the model for a similar situation in the comedy film "Fletch Lives" with Chevy Chase.

Aside from these television antics, during my life in the USA I had a number of experiences in which proponents of what I call perverted Christianity crossed my path, and left a bitter taste. I'll detail one of those here:

When I was 13 years old, my mother had been divorced for a couple years. She was dating a man called Mike. They were seeing each other quite regularly, and wo, for awhile there it looked as though this dictator was going to become my new dad. He was a devout born again Christian and belonged to a sect called "The House of Worship." He was also a large and domineering man who persuaded my mother that when disciplining her children, she should use a rod, liberally. He even supplied her with some tools to beat us with. There were different belts and boards, with labels on them. Each had its specific use for a specific "sin" which we the children were bound to commit. Needless to say, rod or no rod, I was still just as self-willed as I wanted to be and if I essayed to do something that would warrant the use of a prescribed rod against me, well it was simply all the more important not to get caught. My brother Brendan and I once thought we had a solution, which was to gather up all the boards and straps, and get rid of them in trash dumpster down the street, which we did one day when our mother was gone to work. Well, that didn't work of course. Mike simply showed up with a new supply, but this time, an additional one was added bearing the label, "removing a rod from its hanging place," and that one got used on us first for the above confessed sin.

I recall one evening, for reasons unknown to me at the time, Mike invited me to go with him for a drive. "Nowhere in particular," he said. We ended up parked in the parking lot of an A&W Rootbeer Restaurant. He started talking to me about Jesus. I recall that he somehow exerted an unrighteous influence over me, compelling me to get down on the floor of his car and recite words which he would dictate, such as "Jesus I just praise you. I know I'm a sinner and always will be a sinner. You yourself have said there's nothing I can do to change this, and so I accept you into my heart, as my personal saviour..." I'll never forget the bitter, bitter spirit which pervaded this session. It was not of God. It was not of Christ. It was evil. I am sure of that.

Mike was on an ego trip. I remember times when, reclining back on the couch in our living room he would piously exhale and say to my mother, "I saved a man last night" and then with a wearied yawn, "I was up till two a.m. bringing him to Jesus. It wasn't easy, but I saved him." Mike was into "saving" people and I became one of his conquests. From further experience in life, I have learned that this practice was not unique simply to Mike. It goes with the trade. This act of "saving people," compelling them to accept Jesus as their personal Saviour under the above described conditions is a common practice of various infected strains of evangelism.

As for me, I felt violated. Even with the passing years the bitterness and vile tincture of that experience has not faded. Looking back, it is all rather insignificant, yet the event remains unforgettable and wrong. Indeed it seems like a kind of spiritual assault where the abuser extracts a dose of personal gratification, while the victim is left feeling stripped and ashamed.

An unfortunate result of nonsense and corruption which goes on under the ruse of religion is that many clear thinking people are put off the subject altogether, rejecting truth as well as the falsehoods.

With regards to *true religious doctrine* as opposed to *false doctrine*, let us consider the following example which demonstrates the fixed nature of truth vs. error.

We shall focus our attention for a moment upon a glass window and further specify that the kind of glass we are talking about is that of an average household window. This will shatter to pieces if we were to strike it with a solid object. However, if we pour petrol onto a pane of glass such as this and ignite it, the glass would not be consumed and the fluid would simply burn off. This is reality. Now let us suppose that a man comes along who declares that the glass is wood and genuinely believes it to be so. He teaches that if you or I were to throw a rock at it, the rock would simply bounce away as it would off of a standard sheet of half inch plywood.

Imagine that this man builds up a following of one thousand members, which increases to five thousand and even a million people who, with him, believe that this glass is wood. They believe it with all their hearts. They are sincere and mean no harm to anyone. Now, the question is: Does this make it true? Does the fact that so many people are convinced that this piece of glass is wood make it so, or are they wrong?

The answer of course, is they are wrong, believing something which is not true regardless of how strong or sincere that belief may be. The truth would be abruptly revealed as soon as someone chucked a brick through the window.

A perfect historical example of this point appears as we consider that all of Europe once believed the Earth to be flat. Nevertheless, no matter how great their number, the people's belief did not make the Earth become flat in reality. Thus when

Columbus sailed off to prove the world was round, he did not reach the edge and fall off as many supposed he would.

A simple, yet compelling principle comes to view here. If Columbus had been literally the only man on Earth who believed it was round, while everyone else maintained it was flat, then one man would have been right and all the rest of the human race, wrong.

This principle applies also to religion. Simply because a vast number of people believe a particular thing, this does not necessarily mean that it is true. The precise nature of truth vs. error in religion extends much further than the basic question of whether or not there is a God. For instance, if one Christian denomination teaches that Christ is an incorporeal being and exists only in a spiritual form in the hearts of men and women, while on the other hand, another church teaches that Christ is a resurrected being with a physical body, then we have a conflicting doctrine. Thus the question may be raised as to which version is right. Many people feel that it is not possible to find out the correct answers to such queries. Indeed, without divine revelation they remain unsolved mysteries.

In spite of all the fraud, hypocrisy and deception which goes on in the name of religion, there are of course people whose intentions are honest and pure. However we still come up against the question of whether or not the doctrine which they espouse is true — no matter how sincere they may be.

In the face of a bewildering score of different religious persuasions, the search for truth becomes stifling. To a large extent, people in the world have had their sentiments towards religion seared with a hot iron as it were for reasons illustrated earlier in this chapter. We would do well therefore to consider deeply the words of Jesus as he went forth among the people teaching divine truths; "Seek and ye shall find, knock and it shall be opened unto you." (Matthew 7:7-8 and 3 Nephi 14:7-8). Also the words of James the apostle; "If any of you lack wisdom, let him ask of God, that giveth to all men liberally, and upbraideth not; and it shall be given him." (James 1:5)

Does God exist? Does Christ live? Is the actual Church of Jesus Christ upon the earth? Are there twelve apostles upon the earth today, divinely appointed by Him as in ancient times to lead that Church? Is the doctrine of the pre-mortal existence true?

 *131*

"Seek and ye shall find
Ask and it shall be given you
Knock and it shall be opened unto you
By the power of the Holy Ghost,
ye may know the truth
of all things"

Tomorrow's Dreams

Picture this: It is the year 1428. You are in the market square of the town of Salamanca, Spain. A crowd is gathered around a man whose speech is obviously causing no small stir among the people.

He proceeds to declare that "the time will come when people from all walks of life, will sit within the walls of their own houses and look upon a silver plate — which at the command of a fingertip shall ignite as it were with light! And then shall open unto them a vision of things from all around the world. Men shall speak to them from great distances through this plate. Even from the far side of the vast unmeasured sea, shall men speak, and the people with these instruments shall both see and hear."

The crowd quickly becomes agitated with this man. Some begin to ridicule; "perhaps he has been eating hemlock in small doses" shouts a burly man from the doorway of his butchery. Others begin to consult privately among themselves: "He is in league with witches," whispers the town judicator.

The man continues his declaration saying: "Our children's children will construct huge vessels like giant hollow tree trunks made of iron, which by the command of a man will shoot forward and rise off of the ground, carrying hundreds of people. And this shall they do as a means of swift transportation from place to place."

One of the hecklers in the crowd, laughing loudly, blurts out; "What! you mean our descendants shall fly through the sky as birds?"

"No" says the man. "They shall fly through the sky as gods! The sound of their wings shall be as a thousand running horses amidst a mighty wind! Fire and smoke shall issue forth of their mighty outstretched arms."

The orator is now in big trouble with the ruling class and the religious hierarchy. "He has spoken blasphemy! Heresy! He has said that men shall have the power of Gods."

The 'heretic' continues: "Men shall cause objects great and tall, of enormous weight to rise into the sky and go forth speedily even unto the moon. These objects, at the command of men, will set down gently on the moon and men will emerge. They shall walk upon the moon and return again."

The crowd is now enraged. The foreteller will soon be arrested, tried and sentenced for his crimes. Just before being taken away, one of the scornful onlookers shouts, "Tell us old man, is this all of your fantasies or is there yet more!?" "Much more!" he replies. "The time will come when people will carry a device in their hand — through which they will be able to speak to anyone whom they choose — even if it be someone on the far side of the world. They will converse and be heard plainly by one another even if a thousand leagues lie between them." Before the strange old man can continue, he is taken and cast into prison pending judgement.

Now we may ask, why were the people so incensed with the speaker in this scenario? It is because he was making declarations which challenged the standard views of the time.

The point to be taken here is simply that things which are standard in our modern lifestyle, would have been totally inconceivable to people in former centuries. By the same token, advances will yet unfold upon us which at present are inconceivable and thought of as scientifically impossible. One of these, is the resurrection of our bodies from death to an immortal and incorruptible state.

Many people in today's world view this subject as a mere tenet of religion when in reality, this will be the greatest universal transformation to come upon mankind. Everyone, regardless of race, religion, or any other factors will be brought forth in the resurrection.

The thought of a planet inhabited by superior beings with extraordinary powers sets the the stage for an elaborate science fiction fantasy. Yet this is precisely the destiny that lies ahead for the human race, though at present, such an existence is beyond our understanding. The prophet Joseph Smith saw those future kingdoms. By the gift and power of God he was given a vision of the different degrees of glory to which mankind shall attain. Of even the lowest kingdom of glory he remarked; "And thus we saw, in the heavenly vision, the glory of the telestial, which surpasses all understanding." (Doctrine and Covenants 76:89)

If the suggestion, for example, was put forward that you and I shall one day have the ability to travel by the power of thought, and could will ourselves to be standing on the surface of the planet Venus, with no harm to our bodies, such an assertion would of course be received as utter fantasy. Comparatively, the idea of a remote controlled entertainment centre complete with television, satellite dish, VCR, radio, cassette, CD, and 80 watt sound surround speakers, would have been utter fantasy to people living in 1601, yet for us it is reality.

The following story is a mixture of fact and fiction, doctrine and drama, certainty and speculation. It takes on the challenge of portraying certain aspects of life after the temporal period of the earth is finished. The endeavour to render a ficticious account such as this and have it be realistic, presents a goal which is bound to be missed. At least for me it does, because I cannot comprehend this future existence. At the same time however, I know the resurrection shall come to pass. It is inevitable. The narrative therefore, serves as a format to carry a number of compelling ideas:

After Earth

The surface of Mercury was inhospitable when I was mortal. But now, standing atop a towering ridge, I enumerate jagged rocky peaks which extend in a great circle, twenty kilometres in diameter. Below, a magnificent crater which attests the impact of a massive meteor.

I leap from my perch, two kilometres above the floor of the Corbian basin and fall controllably downward. With the power of thought, I direct my descent towards a vast plain of stone. The surface, except for a myriad of cracks is smooth for several kilometres in every direction. Standing here, I cast an extraordinarily long shadow because of the angle and intensity of the sun's light.

The sun looks twice as large as it used to appear from earth. The intense plasma wave which blows violently outward from the sun is deflected only marginally by the weak magnetic sphere of this planet. So I intensify the aura of my body to shield myself from the onslaught of highly charged particles which if allowed to pass through me would cause an annoying tingling sensation, harmless nevertheless. I experience therefore, a glorious contrast to the time when I was mortal. A time when a simple thing as these solar rays would have been utterly lethal to me or any other man. Not to mention the extreme brightness and heat that washes over me here.

I have stopped off at Mercury on my way to Peren, to take measurements of the convection zone of Mercury's iron based core. This is useful because it represents a prime example of the dipole magnetic field in its 'f' stage. After completing my observations, I transfer once again to Peren. This planet, located in the Thoren system is 92.351 light years from Earth.

Giant reptiles roam this terra firma—which in its primeval stage is a precise model of what earth was like when dinosaurs ruled.

During my life it was entertaining and enlightening for people to attempt to reconstruct and simulate the pre-historic environment of Earth. But now we see that what we envisioned from fossilised records, enhanced with imagination, was only a fragmentary view. Many things about the primeval world did not leave a detectable imprint on the geological record of the earth. Hence we failed to take certain factors into account.

One interesting aspect of Peren is the H^2O canopy. Fully enveloping this planet, in the upper atmosphere, is a dense layer of moisture. This is one of the environmental keys to the way things develop here. Primarily because of the manner in which the sun's rays are filtered while at the same time, other solar effects are retained and distributed evenly around the globe.

There is not a mortal man on Peren at present, but if there was, he could live to be eight or nine hundred earth years old, because of the filtered solar rays.

The planet is a tropical paradise uniformly from the equator to its polar regions. It never rains anywhere upon the face of this orb, but instead, a mist carrying minerals rises up from the ground and nurtures the lush primeval forests. What we have here is an optimum green-house effect.

The time will come however, when the water canopy will develop a large hole over both polar regions. The cause of this separation has to do with the meridional field lines of the planet's dipole magnetic configuration, and their interaction with the solar wind. The charged particles which concentrate at the magnetic poles will, over time, wear away the canopy over these areas. The openings will break the continuity of the global green-house effect which now prevails. The warmth which remains constant throughout* will disseminate, causing the polar regions to change into frozen wastelands. Massive ice caps will form at both poles. A vast change will *take place in the vegetation and animal life of the planet when this occurs.*

*Note: A most elementary observation on how the atmosphere of a planet may preserve and distribute the warmth of the sun may be seen as we consider for example, Mercury. On average, the orbit of Mercury is 58 million km from the Sun. When the Mariner 10 probe passed by Mercury in 1974 it measured temperatures as high as 800°F (427°C) on the day side of the planet, while on the side facing away from the sun, temperatures were as low as minus 343°F (-173°C). In comparison, the Earth is over 149 million kilometres from the sun, yet how cold does it get for us at night? Notwithstanding the fact that we do see variations in temperature around the planet, our atmosphere effectively retains and distributes some degree of warmth around the world. If not for our atmosphere, day-time temperatures on earth would reach about 230°F, and at night they would plummet to as low as 343°F below zero.

When the membrane of the H²O canopy severs in the atmosphere over the magnetic poles, many species of animal and plant life which abound here at present will be extinguished. The canopy will then assume the form of a great belt around the planet, spanning from about Latitude 30° North to about 30° South. Therefore a separation between the waters in the upper atmosphere and the waters of the terrestrial plane will endure for a time longer. According to the will of the creator however, the remaining belt of the canopy will come down in due time as a great torrential rain which will virtually submerge the primordial body of land on this planet.

Thereafter, as the water dissipates and is redistributed through the ecosystem, land will re-appear. When the belt rained down on earth, it caused what became historically known as the "flood of Noah."

I stand here watching with interest as massive creatures in the distance graze upon the upper leaves of trees. The misty haze which settles in the valley gives the impression that these giants are standing in the clouds. A pterodactyl with a wing span of over sixteen feet glides overhead. The fossilised remnants of pterodactyls found on earth led us to believe that a wing span of about eight feet was as big as these creatures ever grew.

Absorbed in the scenes of Peren, I become aware suddenly that Lars is coming. My thoughts reach out to welcome him and then he is here. He greets me with a handshake and a friendly punch in the arm. "What brings you to Peren?" I ask.

"Just a social visit actually. I thought I'd come and see how your studies are going."

"Well... this is a pleasant surprise. I thought you were involved in the trans-field binary amalgamation project at the Saulton vortex over in the Tarragon quadrant."

"Yes, that's right but all the component masses have been set in place now. All we can do now is sit back and wait for the natural course of things to take effect."

"Shall we go sit and wait up there?" I said, pointing to a rocky cliff in the distance.

Lars, quick as always to latch on to my humour returned with: "No, I think if we stand over there among those trees we could watch as they become a petrified forest, while waiting for the binary elements in the Saulton vortex to amalgamate."

Lars and I chuckled over our quips and without the need of speech, agreed to indeed go up to the precipice which I had pointed out, just to sit, talk, and appreciate the wonders of the terrestrial world before us.

I leaned back and with the mighty force of thought which I and fellow resurrected beings possess, soared upward, outward, over the valley and then up to the cliff. Lars was already there and in jest said "pretty fancy!"

"Flying is more fun than just transferring" I replied.

"True—but if it is so fun, let me see you 'fly' from here to earth" he added.

"No thanks. For distances so great, I'll stick to transference."

We sat quietly for a moment looking over this beautiful world. I was also reflecting on the exhilaration and glory which fills my soul always — and also my peers. For in our resurrected state, fatigue, illness, danger, fear and all such things are non-existent. No-one in mortality realised just how tremendous it would be to receive the transformation promised by the Saviour. No-one knew what it would be like to have power of movement within the celuan dimension — which makes instantaneous transference possible regardless of distance. Even across light years of distance.

I was in these thoughts when Lars brought up the subject of our now long past mortal period on earth.

"You know for a while there, we were somewhat anxious over you."

"Why? What do you mean Lars?"

"Well, I mean in mortality. When you were... shall we say distracted. Distracted from your foreordained labours."

"Oh that," I replied half interestedly.

"Face it Cornelias, you were our only hope as far as we knew at the time. Until the genealogical links and sacred ordinances were completed, our progress was stunted.

You were the one, who was born in the right place and the right time in the dispensation of the fullness of times, with access to sufficient resources to search out our names and establish the required links in the physical world."

"How was I to have known? It was not easy for a man living in the 21st century to comprehend the importance of the links between him and his ancestors.

When I first glanced across your name in my mother's genealogical papers I must admit you were nothing more than a name. Lars Anderson. Born, 1673, in Bornholm, Denmark.

It never occurred to me that after mortality, you and the others would come to me with eternal sentiments of gratitude, thanking me for having established the links. I never dreamed that you and I would become such great friends."

"Yes but you did dream something, didn't you?"

I thought for a moment about what Lars could be referring to. And then, I knew. Looking steadfastly in my eyes he said, "you remember don't you."

"Yes", I replied pensively. "That night (in mortality) when I was living in London, when I had that dream,.... it was you wasn't it?"

"Yes, it was."

"Then who were the other six or seven spirits that came into my room with you."

"They were Jeppe and Kirsten, Peder and Malene, Michel and Zicile. You met them after you finished mortality, remember?"

"How could I forget! They all kissed and hugged me and thanked me and made me feel as if to some degree, I had been their Saviour — because of the temple work which had been done on their behalf.

But why in the night vision was I not allowed to see any of your faces?"

"Cornelias, when we began to have serious doubts that you were ever going to get around to your divinely appointed task, we petitioned Heavenly Father for permission to come and give you a bit of a push. Now as you know, the rules on interference from the spirit world into the mortal world were very stringent and had to be so. Hence, the full extent of our permission was only for you to perceive us in your dream, and I was allowed to take your hand and tell you that we were waiting. Indeed, we had waited almost 200 earth years for those ordinances."

"You know Lars, as I think back on my life, it now appears interesting that a binder full of genealogical information which my mother gave me at the age of thirteen, managed to stay with me through all the years.

As a young man I moved house many times to different locations in the United States. Each time, more and more of my old belongings would be lost or left behind.

Along the way even my most favoured possessions seemed to vanish in due course. Stamp collections, coin collections, prized fossils and rock specimens, record albums and many other such things came and went. Then when I moved to England, I left behind just about everything. All I could take was within my luggage limit on the airline. In spite of all this, after ten years in England, having moved many times in that country as well, this cumbersome heavy binder of genealogy was still with me. That binder, which is where I first saw your name seems to have been a catalyst in bringing me to finally completing the genealogical work."

Lars just smiled as I told him this, as if he knew something that I was not aware of about the events. He then told me of similar circumstances in the lives of others, including the following: "Soon after our living descendants completed the sacred temple ordinances on our behalf, I, along with Anders, Jeppe, Michel

and nine others received our resurrection. The
glorious reunion of our spirits to our renewed
physical bodies took place when you were forty —
two years old in mortality. In any case, when it
was the earth year 2004, there was a man in
our Walker line, who was a twelfth generation
nephew to me, living in Scotland. He had
come to an impasse with his genealogical work.
His name was Andrew.

Andrew's delay was holding up a large
amount of other related work which needed to go
ahead, therefore, intervention from our side
became expedient. I was instructed to produce a
marriage certificate for the ancestor he was
unable to locate. I was allowed to place the
certificate in a brown envelope and set it on the
ground in the path he would be walking, en route
to his bus stop. I'll never forget his face when
coming upon the envelope, compelled by curiosity
he picked it up and looking inside found the
marriage certificate which contained the
information of Jon Erikson born May 12,
1521, Stockholm Denmark.

Andrew was absolutely dumbfounded for he
immediately recognised the information as
pertaining to his crucial missing link. He
looked around as if expecting to see some

friendly prankster nearby. I watched with joy as he then proceeded on his way — breathless and in awe, endeavouring to grasp the miracle that had just occurred. He, like you and many others, received assistance from beyond the veil in the task of completing the ancestral files. In Andrew's case however, I was instructed that he could not retain the certificate, thus after he had entered the precious information into the ancestral file in his computer, I removed the paper from him when he left his notebook unattended on a counter-top at the Public Records Office. He was mystified, and I, felt just a bit like a prankster after all."

Lars and I passed a few Peren hours reminiscing about our mortal time, entertaining each other with stories. He had been a craftsman of horse carriages in eighteenth century Denmark, and I, had been through several occupations in the twentieth century. I marvelled at the hardship which people of his time were called to endure. And Lars marvelled at the pressures and complex concerns which those in my time had to bear.

At the same time that I am here with Lars exploring Peren, I am in communication with my beloved wife who is many light years away, enjoying a recreational adventure.

Recently, she has taken up an interest in skiing of all things! Yes, skiing. Snow and all. She enjoys going with her friends to a planet called Ranur for this activity.

While relaxing atop this rocky precipice, overlooking one of Peren's lush valleys I reflect upon the great contrast between the abilities I now possess, compared to the stifling limitations I and everyone else faced in mortality. The things I can do now which are as natural as breathing, were unthought-of then, and never even occured to our imaginations. Not only physically do I surpass all former expectations, but in cosmic consciousness also! The marvellous expansion of the mind which has come to me as well as to all who have received an inheritance with Christ, and in Christ, enthralls the soul and contributes to the everlasting fulness of joy which we feel.

After meditating silently upon these marvels for a time, I turned to Lars to strike up a conversation: "By the way Lars, I noticed that even when the temporal existence of Earth was finished you did not revert to your pre-mortal name. Most people felt that taking up their primordial name was part of coming home again.

I'm curious, why have you not gone back to using 'Mahaleel', your first name?"

"Would you believe, I don't know. I have no reason. I just felt like keeping my earthly name. I suppose, for me, I wanted something more to hang on to in remembrance of my mortal experience."

"That's interesting. For me it was the other way around. I was eager to forget my ordeal in mortality."

"Oh c'mon," Lars chided, "it couldn't have been that bad."

"Well, you're right, it wasn't so bad. I'm just so relieved that I made it out of there without losing my inheritance. I really thought, many times along the way, that it was impossible for me to achieve what Heavenly Father required."

Lars then accompanied me in assimilating further geophysical observations on Peren. The purpose of this, pertains to the acquisition of knowledge. As resurrected beings, we are at liberty to amass knowledge according to our desires. Of course, the fullness of this liberty is found only by those who have an inheritence with Christ.

"Lars, I need to implement one more astro-geophysical test here, and then I will return to Azimure. Could you please assist? The test structure will require priesthood administration?"

"Sure, what do you have mind?"

"We shall increase the axial rotation of Peren by 2 degrees, and elongate the orbit of Peren's moon to an ellipse of 78.9 by 62.12. I shall then return at regular intervals to monitor the resultant changes which occur throughout this ecosystem."

"I would be honoured to assist in the ordinance."

We raised our hands and instituted the changes, by the authority vested in us, after the order of the Firstborn — The Holy One. This was done in accordance with the will of the Father, for all priesthood ordinances and operations, in any instance, are subject to the divine will and omnipotence of our beloved Eternal Father.

Though we have individual freedom, and liberty to develop and pursue our interests, we are yet one with the Father. By Him, we have a fullness of joy. By Him we have this eternal life.

We were about to leave Peren, when Lars suggested going for a swim in the sea. "Yes, that would be great!" I replied. For although we have unrestricted mobility by the power of thought, physical exercise is still a beneficial element in our well-being. We leapt into the air and jetted toward the coast. Lars started playing around and accelerated. Then I matched his speed. We made it a game to complete the journey of 1450 kilometres while yet staying within 150 metres of the planet surface. That was a challenge when coming up against mountainous regions. We then plunged into the sea. After swimming on the surface for a while, we darted under in search of interesting features. The deeper abysses didn't hold much excitement, but we did find some extraordinary crinoid forests. And then Lars was clowning about, riding on the back of a plesiosaur. I tried to out-do him by commandeering a giant Manta, but the moment I mounted the creature, it zoomed straight to the bottom and endeavoured to bury itself in the sand of the sea floor.

After our recreation, Lars and I stood together on the sea floor. Our souls filled with joy and gladness, as always. We bowed our heads in prayer to Heavenly Father, thanking him for the beauty and the joy of our existence. We then entered the celuan dimension and at the same instant stepped onto the beautiful golden pavement of our home district, *Azimure,* on earth.

We conversed a few minutes more. Out of our entire lineage, along with *Zelahnim,* *Lars* is one of my closest friends. This might not have been, if in mortality I had not done my part in assembling the genealogical links. Who would have thought that after earth, I could become best friends with someone whom I never knew on earth, but nevertheless, was as much a part of my family as my grandfather, grandmother or grandson is etc. *Lars,* my great - great - great - great - great - great - great - great - great - great grandfather.

Azimure is the principal abode of my lineage, and is a component of the great and mighty city of *Zion,* the boundaries of which, extend over the whole earth.

Walking towards my estate, I see the resplendent crystal mansion which *Alecia* and I have fashioned according to our dreams. *Alecia,* my beautiful wife, appears at my side. We embrace and walk together across the spacious gardens of our estate.

❖ ❖ ❖

While there are yet many roads to explore in the celestial world of Cornelias, Alecia, Lars and the other glorious resurrected beings of Azimure, it cannot suffice to merely whip up a work of fiction here. For although the story consists of fabricated details, specific axioms are touched upon which are already nearly lost in a sea of fable.

The story is set in a time when the inhabitants of the earth have all been resurrected to immortality. The seventh millennium is past, and the earth, from its core to its mantle has been melted down with fervent heat and has arisen as a magnificent gem stone — like a Phoenix from the ashes. The inhabitants, are those who have "inherited the earth" and now as resurrected beings, live in perpetual glory and joy which our present imagination and language cannot begin to assimilate.

The earth, in its celestialised form, somehow functions as a great translator, a Urim and Thummim by which the inhabitants are able to receive knowledge concerning many things. Things which do not occur to our imagination at present, therefore we cannot even attempt to list the type of revelations which the celestialised earth will give to its possessors.

A diamond, before coming to that form is a piece of coal. The transformation process involves extreme heat and pressure. Consider also what becomes of sand when subjected to similar conditions; it becomes glass. After the seventh millenium, the elements which comprise our earth will undergo a similar transformation, the result being comparable perhaps to the substance of an emerald, a sapphire, jasper, topaz and such like.

As a piece of coal is transformed into a beautiful diamond, so shall the earth be transformed into a higher state. Earth shall be imbued with the glory of the Lord, insomuch that this planet, shall one day be resplendent, as the sun is resplendent. If these projections seem unfounded, contemplate Revelation chapter 21, and Isaiah chapter 60.

A fundamental precept featured in the *After Earth* story is the resurrection. The power and impact of this concept where you and I are concerned rests in the aforementioned fact, that every single one of us will be resurrected.

❖   ❖   ❖

I recently saw an interesting situation in a billboard advertisement for the National Lottery. A man, obviously in a critical condition of health, was shown laying in a hospital bed clutching a lottery ticket, wildly dreaming of winning the jackpot.

This led me to contemplate how all the money in the world would not yield the pleasures hoped for if one is in extremely poor health, notwithstanding the point that abundant financial resources can be of tremendous benefit to people who are disabled or in ill health.

Let us consider the following proposal: In one year's time, you are going to win twenty million pounds cash, tax free. You are forty years old and in good health, so there is still time to enjoy the money. Thus you have exciting plans of travelling all over the world, seeing the sights and buying things. You will buy cars, yachts, and houses, TV's and stereos, computers and virtually everything you want.

While the thrill of this may be great, you will however, in the recesses of your soul feel certain longings. A faint emptiness which the trappings of money cannot fill.

In spite of your limitless supply of funds, the aches and pains of mortality will yet nip at your heels. You continue to grow old. The wings of time carry you ever closer to the inevitable end of your monetary paradise. An end which you are not eager to see.

Now let us bring to view a second proposal: Never mind striking it rich in the lottery or by any other burst of luck. You will have to carry on in life with whatever level of wealth you currently have, or do not have.

Let us suppose however that you are guaranteed, say, eight years from now, to be physically transformed. Magnificently transformed! Your body will become superior beyond your greatest expectations. You will grow to a state of eternal youth and remain everlastingly vibrant, energetic and beautiful. Pain will be non-existent.

Scientists have determined that a large part of the human brain is dormant and remains untapped throughout our lives. It has been said that we use only ten percent of our brain's capacity. In your new superior condition this potential will become active. You now have extraordinary abilities which include being able to pass through matter and travel at will to distant places in the instant of a thought.

With a powerful sense of well being, harbouring no fears and absolutely no financial concerns, with the extent of the galaxy at your fingertips, you soar indestructibly and everlastingly through eternity.

Considering these two options, if you could have one of them, which would you choose? For me, the second proposal is by far the greatest. And the reality is; that every person will receive this transformation, albeit we may fail to achieve its full potential.

This rejuvenation is brought about through the atonement of Jesus Christ, yet some Christian denominations do not fully understand the doctrine of the resurrection. Some are under the misconception that it is conditional upon faith or personal merits. This is accurate only to the extent that reaching our utmost potential in the resurrection is dependant on our performance in applying principles of virtue, truth and righteousness in our lives. The Bible is clear however *"that all shall be made alive."* (1 Corinthians 15:22). Furthermore, in John Chapter 5 we read:

> Marvel not at this: for the hour is coming, in the which all that are in the graves shall hear his voice.
>
> And shall come forth; they that have done good unto the resurrection of life; and they that have done evil unto the resurrection of damnation.
>
> St. John 5:28-29

The scriptural term "damnation" has also been misunderstood by people supposing that damnation is synonymous with a lake of fire and brimstone and the depths of Hell. The general implication of this term however is most easily illustrated by simply considering the role of a river dam. In such a case, the river is dammed. Stopped in its progress. A different word but the same concept applies in the "damnation" of the human soul, although it is of course not entirely as simple as that.

The ancient prophets in America held a detailed understanding of the resurrection — hence we may benefit from their writings in the Book of Mormon on the subject:

> Now, there is a death which is called a temporal death; and the death of Christ shall loose the bands of this temporal death, that all shall be raised from this temporal death.

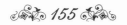

> The spirit and the body shall be reunited again in its
> perfect form; both limb and joint shall be restored to its
> proper frame, even as we now are at this time; and we
> shall be brought to stand before God, knowing even as we
> know now, and have a bright recollection of all our guilt.
>
> Now, this restoration shall come to all, both old and
> young, both bond and free, both male and female, both the
> wicked and the righteous; and even there shall not so
> much as a hair of their heads be lost...
>
> Alma 11: 42-44

The above quoted verse for example, goes on to declare that
upon the resurrection, every soul shall stand before God "to be
judged according to their works, whether they be good or
whether they be evil."

One other caution we should take to heart may be illustrated
using clay as an example. The potter or sculptor, in the process
of creating, may shape and reshape, mould and remould the
entity in his hands at will. Even if the clay was to dry out, it
could be made malleable again with some patience and effort
by soaking and breaking it down in water. Once the clay object
has gone through the kiln however, this is no longer possible.
The substance of the clay becomes fixed permanently.

Certain scriptural passages give credence to the suggestion
that our resurrection will be the catalyst to our kiln. Right now
in mortality, we can develop and change our character for better
or worse. The ominous probability looms however, that the
attitudes and aberrations, virtues and vagaries, tendencies and
traits, will's and wont's etc. which we form in this life, will
solidify somewhat in the resurrection. Thus, even though we
shall all be raised to immortality, we should not be lulled into a
false sense of absolution regarding the consequences of our
actions.

The most basic fact is that we shall be raised to immortality
— and never die physically again. One valuable scripture on
the resurrection is found in Philippians 3:20-21, wherein it is
written that *"...the Saviour, the Lord Jesus Christ ...shall
change our vile body, that it may be fashioned like unto his
glorious body, according to the working whereby he is able
even to subdue all things unto himself."* With this in view we

may observe what Christ was able to do in his resurrected state and contemplate how these things may apply to ourselves in the future.

In the the Book of Luke, it is written that when the disciples were in a closed room the Saviour appeared:

> And as they thus spake, Jesus himself stood in the midst of them, and saith unto them, Peace be unto you.
>
> But they were terrified and affrighted, and supposed that they had seen a spirit.
>
> And he said unto them, Why are ye troubled? and why do thoughts arise in your hearts?
>
> Behold my hands and my feet, that it is I myself: handle me, and see; for a spirit hath not flesh and bones, as ye see me have.
>
> Luke 24: 36-39

Thus we may ask; How did the Lord *appear* suddenly in their midst, while still possessing the tangible aspect of flesh and bone? Likewise shall we be able to do.

The Saviour according to the record took *"a piece of a broiled fish, and of an honey comb... and did eat before them."* Thus we see that in our resurrected state we may still eat. Yet seeing that we cannot die, it remains difficult to assess how the consumption of food fits into the picture.

One of the key factors in the concept of our being raised to an immortal state is that instead of blood flowing through our veins there will be a much superior substance. Blood is one of the most corruptive things in us.

When Jesus completed his ministration among the Jews, he ascended up into heaven. Moreover, when after his resurrection he came to the ancient inhabitants of America, he first appeared in the sky: *"...and behold, they saw a man descending out of heaven; and he was clothed in a white robe; and he came down and stood in the midst of them; ..."* (3 Nephi 11:8).

Thus, we shall have power over the influence of gravity, which highlight's the meaning of the verse quoted earlier from Philippians; *"...whereby he is able even to subdue all things unto himself."* This concept has also been demonstrated in a number of other applicable situations. Take for example the incident of the visit of the resurrected Moroni to Joseph Smith in 1823. Moroni stood in the air, for his feet did not touch the floor. This event to provides a magnificent precedent from which we may draw information.

Moroni was a prophet, who lived on the American continent about 1,400 years ago. As a resurrected being, he was sent for a divine purpose to Joseph Smith, who described the event thus:

> While I was thus in the act of calling upon God, I discovered a light appearing in my room, which continued to increase until the room was lighter than at noon day, when immediately a personage appeared at my bedside, standing in the air, for his feet did not touch the floor. He had on a loose robe of most exquisite whiteness. It was a whiteness beyond anything earthly I had ever seen; nor do I believe that any earthly thing could be made to appear so exceedingly white and brilliant.
>
> Not only was his robe exceedingly white, but his whole person was glorious beyond description and his countenance truly like lightning. The room was exceedingly light, but not so very bright as immediately around his person. When I first looked upon him, I was afraid; but the fear soon left me.
>
> He called me by name, and said unto me that he was a messenger sent from the presence of God to me, and that his name was Moroni...

Bearing in mind that Moroni was once a mortal man, we see vivid fulfilment of the ancient prophecy by Daniel: *"And they that be wise shall shine as the brightness of the firmament..."* (Daniel 12:3). These words are in reference to our potential to be glorious and brilliant in our resurrected state. Can you imagine yourself as a glorious being, virtually full of light, with an intense field of white light emitted by your presence? This potential resides in each of us, as we are the offspring of God the Eternal Father.

In our future state we will radiate a magnificent aura of glory if a sufficient moral standard has been maintained in our lives. It becomes evident though, that a resurrected person may have absolute control over this aura and subdue it at will, insomuch that a glorious being such as this could walk among us totally undetected, having the appearance of a mortal person.

As resurrected beings, the ability to go at will to places beyond current limitations and the celestial views which will expand before us, shall engender a cosmic consciousness and an exhilaration beyond anything our mortal senses have known.

Acknowledging that depending on our choices we may fail to gain the full potential of this transformation, it should nevertheless be compelling to know that come what may, we will be rejuvenated in this way. In the real world though, the here-and-now weighs upon us shoving promises of the future to the side, making them as hard to grasp hold of as the fleeting dreams of sleep.

To highlight other capacities which may be inherent in us in the resurrection, let us use the example of a bullet which is about to be fired from a gun. Your senses are so extraordinarily enhanced and quickened, that to begin with, you are able to look through the atoms which make up the body of the gun and see the bullet inside.

As the hammer strikes, the dimensions of time are so fully within your grasp that you are able to casually watch the bullet travelling out of the gun, as if in slow motion. Supposing this gun was aimed directly at you, watching the bullet as it approaches, you have leisure time to entertain the various options of how you would like to deal with the situation.

You could step aside and let it pass. Or you could exercise the power of thought and communicate to the intelligence comprising the atoms of the bullet, and command it to turn back. On the other hand you could require these atoms to. dissipate.

None of these options are necessary however, for you can simply allow the bullet to pass through you. The effect might be comparable to the way a body of water in a glass would accept the insertion of a pencil, and resume its original form, undamaged after removal of the foreign object.

Having touched upon this subject, it becomes essential to acknowledge the difference between what is called *the first resurrection* and subsequent stages of this fruition of our Heavenly Father's work, and of our sojourn through time.

In fine, those who maintain a sufficient degree of righteousness in their lives will have part in the first resurrection, which has already commenced with the resurrection of Christ. Ever since He rose from the dead, prophets and righteous people of past ages have been and continue to be resurrected.

The first resurrection will occur on a massive scale at the time of Christ's second coming. After this however, as the world progresses through the seventh millennium—the thousand years wherein Christ shall reign personally upon the earth—there will yet remain literally billions of souls in the spirit prison, awaiting resurrection. They will exist in anguish, tormented by each other and by their own fears and regrets in a self-made hell. What a contrast to the delightful existence of the resurrected, dwelling on a renewed, cleansed earth, in its paradisiacal state. (Revelation 20:4-6).

Visualise for a moment the most beautiful, natural paradise location on this entire planet. Whatever your selection, the condition of the whole earth will match this and in some ways even surpass it after Christ's reign is ushered in, and the earth has received its paradisiacal glory. You and I will live and have full felicity in our existence—in the glorious millennium, if we will simply embrace truth, equity, and light, rather than darkness.

At the end of this thousand years, the remaining souls will also be resurrected, at which point the great and last judgement will convene, when we all shall stand before God to be judged and rewarded, according to our works.

The Seventh Thousand Years

A glorious age, unprecedented in all the history of the world is about to dawn upon the earth—the *seventh millennium.* This is not in reference to the turn of the millennium at the year 2000. The commencement of the era referred to will be punctuated by the apocalyptic return of Jesus Christ, whose arrival will be a global event. His coming will be in the clouds of heaven and all nations shall see it:

> And then shall appear the sign of the Son of man in heaven: and then shall all the tribes of the earth mourn, and they shall see the Son of man coming in the clouds of heaven with great glory.
>
> St. Matthew 24:30

> For I will reveal myself from heaven with power and great glory, with all the hosts thereof, and dwell in righteousness with men on earth a thousand years, and the wicked shall not stand.
>
> Doctrine and Covenants 29:11

A visualization of this event may be acquired by reviewing pertinent scriptural references. While somewhat repetitive of the same point, the various passages all have an additional shade of information to offer. A few of which are thus:

> Behold, he cometh with the clouds; and every eye shall see him, and they also which pierced him: and all kindreds of the earth shall wail because of him.
>
> Revelation 1:7

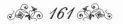

...the day soon cometh that you shall see me, and know
that I am; for the veil of darkness shall soon be rent, and
he that is not purified shall not abide the day.

Doctrine and Covenants 38:8

For the day cometh that the Lord shall utter his voice out
of heaven; the heavens shall shake and the earth shall
tremble, and the trump of God shall sound both long and
loud, and shall say to the sleeping nations: Ye saints arise
and live; ye sinners stay and sleep until I shall call again.

For in mine own due time will I come upon the earth in
judgment, and my people shall be redeemed and shall reign
with me on earth.

For the great millennium of which I have spoken by the
mouth of my servants shall come.

Doctrine and Covenants 43:18, 29-30

...and behold, I will come; and they shall see me in the
clouds of heaven, clothed with power and great glory; with
all the holy angels; ...and the saints that have slept shall
come forth to meet me in the cloud. ...and the saints shall
come forth from the four quarters of the earth. ...and the
earth shall tremble, and reel to and fro, and the heavens
also shall shake.

And the Lord shall utter his voice, and all the ends of the
earth shall hear it; and the nations of the earth shall
mourn, and they that have laughed shall see their folly.

And calamity shall cover the mocker, and the scorner shall
be consumed; and they that have watched for iniquity
shall be hewn down and cast into the fire.

And ...the heathen nations shall be redeemed, and they
that knew no law shall have part in the first resurrection...

And Satan shall be bound, that he shall have no place in
the hearts of the children of men.

... when the Lord shall appear he shall be terrible unto
them ... and they shall stand afar off and tremble.

And all nations shall be afraid because of the terror of the
Lord, and the power of his might.

Doctrine and Covenants 45: 44-46, 47-50, 54-55, 74-75

Then shall two be in the field; the one shall be taken, and
the other left. Two women shall be grinding at the mill;
the one shall be taken, and the other left.

Matthew 24:40-41

We today have the benefit of a retrospective view regarding
Christ, which those in ancient times did not have. There is
sufficient historical evidence to determine indisputably that He
lived and was crucified. The life of Jesus is not a myth or a
legend, it is historical fact. Those people who lived prior to his
birth, yet perceived and believed the prophecies of it, were wise
and correct in their faith. In like manner, those today who
believe and have faith in the prophecies of his coming are right
and will be proven so, in the not to distant future.

In the Book of Genesis, six days or periods are associated
with God's work in the creation of the earth. The Seventh day,
was sanctified and set apart as a day in which he rested from
his labours. A significant precedent is seen in these details.

The scriptures reveal that a total of seven thousand years
shall comprise the temporal existence of man on the earth (See
for example; Doctrine and Covenants 77:6a). Thus, a period
comparable to one week of seven days when held in view with
the words of the ancient apostle, Peter: "...be not ignorant of
this one thing, that one day is with the Lord as a thousand
years, and a thousand years as one day." (2 Peter 3:8)

From the fall of Adam, a specific time allotment for the
earth began. The clock, the timer, engaged. Six new days
commenced in which the Creator would contend with his work.
And what is this great work that should so occupy the
Omnipotent One? To bring to pass the immortality and eternal
lives of those spirits who have been waiting to come to Earth,
whose mortal bodies thus acquired, are formed in the "image
and likeness" of their Creator. And the seventh day will be set
apart as special, according to its precedent. As we move into
the seventh day, He will again rest from his work in that He
will bring it to another plateau of completion and sanctify it.

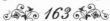

The Seventh Thousand Years

In the year 1830 in a revelation to the prophet Joseph Smith, the Lord said "For behold, the field is white already to harvest; and it is the eleventh hour, and the last time that I shall call laborers into my vineyard." (Doctrine and Covenants 33:3)

What did the Lord mean by the words, *eleventh hour?* The way I see it, this statement reveals that in 1830, we had already reached the "eleventh hour" in the archetype of *Saturday night* in the week of the earth's temporal period. That was over 165 years ago which would mean the dawning of the seventh millennium is virtually upon us. In any case, the inference is that time is short. The Lord has revealed enough that we may conclude without speculation, that the *great and dreadful day of the Lord* is near.

Having said this, we would do well to observe that through the centuries, men have often been too hasty in interpreting the scriptures, trying to pin-point the Second Coming of Christ and other mysteries.

In AD 999 for example, many Christian congregations, according to some sources, began bracing themselves for the end of the world. The doctrine of eschatology imbibed among these groups had promulgated the belief that the second advent of Christ would happen at the turn of the millennium. This was an unequivocal expectation which, among certain pockets of believers precipitated what bordered on mass hysteria. Pilgrimages to the Holy Land, amnesty for prisoners, confession of secrets, and purging towns of known sinners are among some of the fleet-footed preparations which were being made.

However, as might be expected, different historical sources seem to come up with varying slants on what really happened. The *History of Western Philosophy* for example says:

> It is a mistake however, to suppose that a special dread of the end of the world in the year 1000 prevailed at this time, as used to be thought. Christians, from St Paul onward, believed the end of the world to be at hand, but they went on with their ordinary business none the less.

History of Western Philosophy, by Bertrand Russell. 1961 p.394.

What a stark contrast to the *Chronology of World History* by G.S.P. Freeman which declares:

A.D. 1000: End of the world confidently expected.
Widespread famine caused by failure to cultivate
crops.

Chronology of World History, Freeman - Grenville: 1975 p.234

Perhaps one of the more tangible evidences of this
doomsday expectation is the *Blickling Homilies,* a work of
homiletic literature, circulated by the clergy during the years
leading up to A.D. 1000, written largely to prepare people for
the expected end of the world. Nevertheless, we may surmise
that this runaway eschatological observance was limited to
various pockets of believers across Europe. For the most part,
from plebeians to the papacy, life went on as normal.

On into the present, similar scenes have been repeated. The
founder of the Jehovah's Witnesses Church for example,
Charles Taze Russell, convinced himself and his followers that
the world would end in 1874. When nothing happened, the
prediction was revised to 1914, as the year that Christ was
definitely going to come and subdue all governments. Instead,
what we got was World War I. The new object of prophecy
became 1975 and since then, revisions have continued as each
date passes, failing to bring the apocalyptic change.

We could fill a book detailing the failed expectations of
religious establishments and cults which have essayed to predict
the date of Christ's Second Coming.

Here in our present discussion, the last thing we want is to
get entangled with assumptions and speculations which almost
always leave a person holding a bag of erroneous ideas.
However, while acknowledging the Saviour's declaration that no
man knows the day nor the hour of his coming (Matthew 24:36),
we must also acknowledge the following directive:

> Now learn a parable of the fig tree; When his branch is
> yet tender, and putteth forth leaves, ye know that summer
> is nigh: So likewise ye, when ye shall see all these things,
> know that it is near, even at the doors.

Matthew 24:32-33

There are sign posts and parables given by which we may
discern the times in which we live. Even so, if we judge too
hastily, it is easy to misinterpret the signs of the times. In
Matthew Chapter 24 where the Lord outlines these events, He

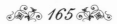

lists "wars and rumors of wars" "famines and pestilences, and earthquakes," "false prophets," hatred among the inhabitants of the earth, etc. etc. I have often seen people look at these things and say that all the signs are coming to pass, citing the fact that we do have famine, pestilence, earthquakes, false prophets and hatred in the world. There is folly in such an interpretation, for indeed, have we not seen all of this since time immemorial? Thus how can these things be signs of the "last days"? Additional insight must be employed if we are to identify properly the calamities referred to in the prophecies.

Not wishing to go into a long essay on this issue, it is sufficient to say that when the actual wave of earthquakes, pestilence, famine and hardship comes which will directly foreshadow the advent of Christ, it will make the world of the 1980s and 90s, with all its troubles, seem like a golden age of peace and plenty.

By the time the Lord God of Israel arrives in the clouds of heaven and is seen by the nations in His majesty, might and power, this world will have gone through drastic changes which have not yet come to pass. Until the ravages of natural upheaval and destruction have gone through and turned illustrious cities into piles of rubble, leaving nations in a state of anarchy, and have produced by-products of famine and pestilence such as the world has not known, the millennial reign of Christ will not have begun.

In any case, whether in the spirit world or living on the earth, we shall all witness the glorious arrival of Jesus Christ with the hosts of heaven:

> And the saints that are upon the earth, who are alive, shall be quickened and be caught up to meet him. And they who have slept in their graves shall come forth, for their graves shall be opened; and they also shall be caught up to meet him in the midst of the pillar of heaven.
>
> Doctrine and Covenants 88:96-97

At the commencement of the transcendent age of Christ's millennial reign, the whole earth shall be cleansed by fire:

> For behold, the day cometh, that shall burn as an oven; and all the proud, yea, and all that do wickedly, shall be

stubble: and the day that cometh shall burn them up, saith the Lord of hosts, that it shall leave them neither root nor branch.

Malachi 4:1

Then shall the righteous who were caught up to meet the Lord come back down to possess the earth, thus bringing literal fulfillment to the prophetic words:

And ye shall tread down the wicked; for they shall be ashes under the soles of your feet in the day that I shall do this, saith the Lord of hosts.

Malachi 4:3

The sabbath of the earth will then follow. It eludes the imagination to perceive how glorious and beautiful this era will be. Endeavouring to formulate a picture of the cleansed, renewed earth, it is important to adhere to the information given in the scriptures and the words of the latter-day prophets. By this, the following considerations may be registered:

In addition to being consummately cleansed, the continents shall become one land *"and the earth shall be like as it was in the days before it was divided."* (Doctrine and Covenants 133:24)

A reliable authority to whom we may turn for enlightenment on this is Bruce R. McConkie, who in 1972, on October 12, was ordained one of the twelve apostles of Jesus Christ. Elder McConkie (1915-1985) served in this capacity for about twelve and a half years until the end of his life:

With the ushering in of the Millennium, "the earth will be renewed and receive its paradisiacal glory"; that is, it will return to the edenic, terrestrial state which existed (when Adam and Eve were in the garden of Eden). In that primeval day, thorns, thistles, briars and noxious weeds had not yet made their appearance; there were no deserts and unfruitful places... but the whole earth was a delightful garden...

The Millennium... will be a "day of transfiguration," a day "when the earth shall be transfigured" (D.&C.63:20-21), a day when the continents and islands shall again "become one land," ...when all things will return to their state of paradisiacal glory.

Mormon Doctrine: "Millennium"

The Seventh Thousand Years

We also learn that *"in the barren deserts there shall come forth pools of living water; and the parched ground shall no longer be a thirsty land."* (Doctrine and Covenants 133:29). Consider the far reaching implications in these words. What would it mean—in terms of global ecological and geological changes—if the deserts of our earth became fertile plains and woodlands? Furthermore; *"The wolf also shall dwell with the lamb, and the leopard shall lie down with the kid; ...and a little child shall lead them. And the cow and the bear shall feed (together); their young ones shall lie down together: And the lion shall eat straw like the ox."* (Isaiah 11:6-7)

This long awaited repose between carnivorous and herbivorous kingdoms will extend not only through mammalia but into the reptile world as well; *"And the suckling child shall play on the hole of the asp (the horned viper), and the weaned child shall put his hand on the cockatrice (also a venomous serpent) den."* (Isaiah 11:8)

Thus in the Millennium, as children play in the beautiful countryside, if perchance they find entertainment by digging in an alluring hole in the ground, which happens to be the den of a poisonous snake or any other dangerous creature for that matter, no ill shall come of it. For the Lord has said:

And in that day the enmity of man, and the enmity of beasts, yea the enmity of all flesh, shall cease from before my face.

Doctrine and Covenants 101:26

The divine foreknowledge given to us in these words becomes more fully efficacious as we take into account the meaning of the word *enmity*, which encompasses all hostility, aggression, animosity, conflict, contempt, malevolence, strife and so on. All of these, according to the Lord's own word, will be done away with throughout the animal kingdom.

Therefore, if the animal kingdom will be thus altered, we may understand that a much different eco-system to that which we know at present will be incumbent. What a beautiful thought to know that we shall no longer need to slaughter animals for sustenance. No more abattoirs and battery chicken farms. It seems to me that various hereditary maladies are forming in some of the world's livestock as a result of the way we mass produce these commodities. In poultry farming for example, generations upon generations of chickens are fed upon meal which is mixed with the ground up bodies of their grandparents, simply because it is more economical for farmers to make use of dispatched stock in increasing the volume of feed for the working stock.

In this life, we scramble about, full of worry and anxiety trying to carve out a niche for ourselves in the material world, coveting this or that place, thinking, 'that is where I would like to be forever.' And even if we are among those fortunate few who gain possession of a piece of what seems like paradise on earth, the duration of our enjoyment of it will be, at best, no more than eighty or ninety years. When compared to the idea of securing a place in the millennial era, eighty years of material opulence in today's hectic, dangerous and troubled world becomes minuscule.

In the present world, you can expend every ounce of energy and all your resources trying to gain or achieve something, which sadly, may yet never be realized because unfortunately, life is not always fair, as epitomized in the following example:

A television documentary called *Dispatches* recently aired the story of a certain Filipino woman, which was typical of countless similar cases wherein people in the Philippines, through lack of worthwhile employment opportunities, enlist in a work abroad scheme which takes them to Saudi Arabia. To cut a long story short, this woman ended up slaving away for various oppressive employers, who took advantage of her situation and made her work without pay. Through leaving her original abusive employer, who under the work agreement held her passport, she became classed as a criminal which compounded her situation. She fled her employer for various reasons, which included being beaten regularly. This woman had children back home in the Philippines whom she of course loved dearly, but had not seen for years—being trapped in Saudi Arabia. Originally, she had merely set out with a noble determination to work hard, sacrificing the comfort of being home with her family, to have a chance at raising some money to give a better future to her children. But this dream turned into a nightmare because of cruel, self-centered, oppressive people. The Lord our God has something to say against this kind of evil: *"And I will come near to you to judgment; and I will be a swift witness against ...those that oppress the hireling in his wages."* (Malachi 3:5)

In the end, it was only through the covert assistance from people involved in the *Dispatches* program that this young mother managed to escape from Saudi Arabia and see her family again—robbed of five years of her life. This woman's case is of course a mere drop in an ocean of human suffering.

This brings to view another important factor. In an earlier chapter *(War in Heaven)* we discussed the reality that roaming to and fro upon the earth are billions of evil spirits, who under the reign of Satan, seek to influnce mankind in a negative manner, inciting the inhabitants of the earth to do evil. A vast measure of 'human suffering' is a direct result of this evil presence. When Christ's reign is ushered in, Satan and his angels of darkness shall be imprisoned. John the Revelator saw this event and described it thus:

> And I saw an angel come down from heaven, having the key of the bottomless pit and a great chain in his hand. And he laid hold on ...Satan, and bound him a thousand years. And cast him into the bottomless pit, and shut him up, and set a seal upon him, that he should deceive the nations no more, till the thousand years should be fulfilled: and after that he must be loosed a little season.

> Revelation 20:1-3

Whomsoever will, may in wisdom implement a marvelous perspective which transcends life's disappointments. While rendering due energies to attaining and holding a proper place in this material world, one may also render due consideration toward securing a place in the glorious Millennium which is soon to be unveiled.

In life there is no guarantee that unforeseen tragedies, injustices and other disappointments will not arise and defeat all our efforts to hold a comfortable place in the world. On the other hand though, the beautiful place we may seek to obtain in the Millennium by embracing truth and virtue in this life, is certain and immutable. The period of sixty or ninety years more or less, which we spend in this life is trivial compared to the thousand years of paradise which will comprise the Millennium.

Imagine the most beautiful stretch of fertile land conceivable, upon which you will design and build a spacious, magnificent dwelling. The walls and pillars you will fashion from huge blocks of exquisite white onyx. For roof tiles, plates of gold will be used. We must bear in mind the possibility that this edifice shall have no need of insulation from heat or cold, for it does not appear that the earth in its paradisiacal state will have winter and summer as we know it, but instead, a perfect everlasting climate, indicative of the garden of Eden.

The difference between living on the earth now as opposed to during the Millennium, will be greater than the contrast between living in the Sahara desert as opposed to dwelling in a fertile, lush valley of Mesopotamia. Having said this, it is pertinent to note the words in Isaiah, Chapter 65, which read: *"And they shall build houses, and inhabit them; and they shall plant vineyards, and eat the fruit of them. ...and mine elect shall enjoy the work of their hands. They shall not labour in vain, nor bring forth for trouble (the efforts of their hands shall not be destroyed, taken, or consumed by others); for they are the seed of the blessed of the Lord, and their offspring with them.*

And it shall come to pass, that before they call, I will answer; and while they are yet speaking, I will hear."

❖   ❖   ❖

In trying to visualize the earth in its sanctified, semi-glorified state, we would perhaps overlook the magnificent effects a newly organised atmosphere might have. Observing even the basic aspect of how crucial our ozone layer is, and the difference it makes to our lives, it must accordingly be acknowledged that we lack awareness of the many superlative options which could be implemented by the Creator with regard to the earth's troposphere, stratosphere, magnetosphere, movements within the core and other variables. A different atmospheric composition could filter, and retain the sun's energy in extraordinarily different ways than at present.

Allusions to changes of this nature are carried in the words: *"And every corruptible thing, both of man, or of ...beasts... upon all the face of the earth, shall be consumed; And also that of element shall melt with fervent heat; and all things shall become new..."* (Doctrine and Covenants, 101:24-25).

The apocalyptic event marking the commencement of the glorious, long awaited, millennial reign of Christ draws near, and indeed is at our doors. While we need not endeavour to pinpoint the precise time of Christ's Second Coming, it is He, who taught in wisdom the parable of the fig tree. (Matthew Chapter 24).

Have the fig leaves represented in the parable begun to spring forth? A firm ground upon which to answer this question is seen as we bring forward one particular verse in Matthew Chapter 24; verse 14:

> And this gospel of the kingdom shall be preached in all
> the world for a witness unto all nations; and then shall the
> end come.

The answer therefore, is yes. This prophecy, which the Lord gave as one of the signs preceding His Second Coming, is being fulfilled in magnificence right before our eyes. Many thousands of missionaries representing the Church of Jesus Christ of Latter-Day Saints are going forth this very moment all around the world. They carry the message of the restoration of the original Church of Jesus Christ upon the earth, organized with twelve apostles at its head, as in ancient times.

The precursory events have begun! Sufficient to evince a firm opinion that this world shall not see the year 2045. The great Millennium will have unfurled upon us by then and under a new, worldwide government, with all the land masses gathered into one body, a new system for the reckoning of years will have been implemented. The head of this global government will be Christ—the Prince of Peace! The government shall be upon his shoulder.

Having commented regarding the nearness of these events, it is pertinent to reiterate the statements given in the center paragraphs on page 166 for the benefit of maintaining a rational perspective on the time invloved.

ℰpilogue

We are immersed in eternity. Though the endless road lies yet before us beyond thresholds untraversed, the soles of our feet do in reality pound the pavement of that highway with each passing day. For it extends in whatever direction we turn, encompassing the past, present and future.

We sometimes blindly imagine eternity as something which *will start later*, but each of us, in our individual course has already commenced traveling long ago. Each day, is a little piece of eternity in hand, in substance like clay, which we mold with the actions of that day.

We have discussed the concept of near-death experiences. If we were to delve deeply into this subject, analysing every detail of what people report from these experiences, we could get carried away on a variety of tangents trying to figure out the meaning of things which pertain to virtually another dimension, about which we know very little.

Our purpose in approaching the subject here is to register one main observation: The spirit lives beyond the death of the body. The emphasis of our consideration of near-death experiences pivots upon the consistently recurring detail epitomized in the words: *"I found myself up near the ceiling, looking down. And there on the table, I could see me. I was no longer in my body."*

The worldwide instances of this scenario are so numerous and the details so precise, that it becomes absolute verification that the spirit does not expire at death. People who refuse to accept this are failing to see the daylight at noon.

Epilogue

How many times do we need to calculate two plus two before we are ready to conclude that the sum is four? Okay, we have been over all of this already in the second chapter, however, the splendid realities and far reaching implications of what we are seeing make it a worthy point to re-emphasize. In the NDE scenario we have proof that there is life after death. Thus in turn, yielding conceptual support for the proposition that our spirits existed prior to the birth of our physical bodies.

Most people have heard the age old phrase, "out of the mouths of babes..." Indeed, where the pre-mortal existence is concerned, out of the mouths of infants have come some profound words. My four-year-old son came out one morning with the declaration; "Mommy, before I came into your tummy to be a baby, I was a biiiiig man, living in the sky with Jesus." Some days later, when out of curiosity my wife and I asked him about "before he was a baby," he obviously didn't remember what he'd said, and his great flash of astuteness was now reduced to; "I was a blue smurf with no hair."

I know of a four-year-old girl who turned to her mother and asked "Why don't we have all the beautiful flowers and rainbows that we had before this world?"

There are other instances I could give where, in various ways, aspects of the pre-mortal existence have been *seen*, but to endeavour to share those things is futile, as they would generally not be believed.

I can support the fact that we should be cautious and reserved when confronted with fantastic claims about spiritually related phenomena. A plethora of publications and movements promulgating various spiritual and "new age" views are in circulation, which in my opinion, are completely erroneous. In the history of mankind, an array of situations may be cited wherein we find entire societies encumbered with fallacious beliefs.

The truth though, about our spiritual origin is before us, however, it seems that many people fail to recognise it and are attracted instead to various shades of alchemy and other forms of intrigue. Could it be that the plain truth is simply not mystifying enough, not immediately gratifying enough, not thrilling enough to appeal to certain base desires?

Regarding our spiritual existence prior to the creation of the world, the following passage of scripture from the book of Abraham, the Patriarch of Israel, is clear and precise:

> Now the Lord had shown unto me, Abraham, the intelligences that were organized before the world was; and among all these were many of the noble and great ones; And God saw these souls that they were good, and he stood in the midst of them, and he said: These I will make my rulers; for he stood among those that were spirits, ...and he said unto me: Abraham, thou art one of them; thou wast chosen before thou wast born.
>
> And there stood one among them that was like unto God, and he said unto those who were with him: ...we will make an earth whereon these may dwell; And we will prove them herewith, to see if they will do all things whatsoever the Lord their God shall command them;
>
> And they who keep their first estate shall be added upon; and they who keep not their first estate shall not have glory in the same kingdom with those who keep their first estate; and they who keep their second estate shall have glory added upon their heads for ever and ever.
>
> The Pearl of Great Price— Abraham 3:22-25

The "first estate" referred to in the above, was our pre-mortal existence. We know that being born into this life means that we successfully "kept the first estate," or in other words, we made sufficient right choices in *the first place* to receive the privilege of having a physical body added unto our spirit. Lucifer and his angels are those who "kept not their first estate." This mortal period is our "second estate."

The point of this book, *The Well of Souls*, is to focus, upon the reality that we are eternal beings—in a moment of testing. As the tip of an iceberg is only a semblance of a far greater unseen magnitude, so also is the following passage of scripture:

> ...Eye hath not seen, nor ear heard, neither have entered into the heart of man the things which God hath prepared for them that love him.
>
> 1 Corinthians 2:9

Epilogue

Imagine a classroom of students taking their exams in Science, Maths and Biology, wherein the students are given along with their test sheets, a duplicate with all the answers filled in. Obviously, this would be a totally futile exercise. Similarly, the probationary nature of this life requires many spaces to be left blank where we would dearly love to have the answers. That time will come however, for as it is written:

> Yea verily I say unto you, in that day when the Lord shall come, he shall reveal all things. Things which have passed, and hidden things which no man knew, things of the earth, by which it was made, and the purpose and the end thereof. Things most precious... that are in the earth ...and in heaven.

Doctrine and Covenants 101: 32-34

The reader will have noticed that many scriptural references in this book come from the work of the prophet Joseph Smith. The *Pearl of Great Price*, the *Doctrine and Covenants*, and the *Book of Mormon* are all books of divine knowledge and revelation which God has sent into the earth in these latter days, through Joseph Smith. Hence, a fundamental issue arises in the debate over whether he was a true prophet, or just another man with a clever way of founding another church. For assorted reasons, many in the world challenge the proposition that Joseph Smith was a prophet of God, hence also the scriptures which the world has received by his hand are rejected by these opponents.

My conviction is that Joseph Smith (1805-1844), was a true prophet of God. A prophet whose mission was foretold over 4000 years ago by Joseph, one of the twelve sons of Israel. Moreover, the book of Isaiah, written so long ago, carries many profound and detailed prophecies regarding Joseph Smith, the prophet whose foreordained task was to bring about a restoration of the ancient Church of Jesus Christ upon the earth in the "latter-days." Joseph fulfilled his mission before martyrdom in 1844.

1995

The Prophet Joseph Smith

The content of this book will undoubtedly appear predominantly, or even entirely religious in nature, which for some people is an automatic turn-off. In my view however, the focus of these topics runs far deeper and extends much further than mere religious rhetoric.

Current issues are involved, not distant dreams in the mists of some unforeseeable future.

If a famous man, say John Wayne or John Lennon for example, who is known to be unquestionably dead was to suddenly rise from the grave with a renewed physical body and extraordinary abilities, this would sweep across the world as the greatest headline news that we have ever heard. People would be amazed and interested. If the man in the story is Christ however, the feat of rising from the dead is suddenly less interesting to many people.

Epilogue

If scientists foresaw, on unmistakable grounds that in fifty years the earth would be transformed into a beautiful paradise with no desert stricken regions, this would be extraordinary news which would place every nation in a state of foremost anticipation. Everyone, would be interested. If on the other hand we approach the same subject on the grounds of scriptural prophecy, our interest wanes and with many people, the doors even slam shut; "If I want religion I'll go to find it at church!"

If it were possible to properly address the subjects contained herein and leave religion entirely out of it, I would gladly have done so, but to accomplish that, would be like trying to discuss the Second Coming of Christ—while at the same time, keeping 'religion' out of it.

This book is about the three paramount questions which pertain to every person on the earth:

1. Where did I come from before birth? Do we suddenly spring into existence, or does our origin precede the visible here-and-now?

2. Why am I here? Does the meaning of life run no deeper than to merely scramble for as much fulfillment as we can get during our days here, and then die? Or is this life a component of a greater span of existence? A caterpillar, through metamorphosis emerges from its cocoon a new and glorious creature—and with wings for flight takes to the skies. Could it be that we likewise shall emerge from mortality?

3. Where am I going? After death, do we simply go out like a candle in the wind? Or after death, will we suddenly find ourselves in company with the generations of people who have gone before us? Will we find ourselves in due course, answering to our eternal judge, for what we have done with our days in mortality?

To shun these questions, and their answers, is not doing oneself any favour. In our society, these matters are too often thrown aside as mere religious trivia, when in fact, they are the essence of being alive, and the keys, to the door, to the road, to the greatest happiness and fulfillment that man can achieve.